JOHN

STEPHEN B. CASSERLY

John

Copyright © 2022 Stephen B. Casserly

Visit our website at
www.StillwaterPress.com
for more information.

First Stillwater River Publications Edition

ISBN: 978-1-958217-40-5

Library of Congress Control Number: 2022914547

Names: Casserly, Stephen B., author.
Title: John / Stephen B. Casserly.
Description: First Stillwater River Publications edition. | Pawtucket,
    RI, USA : Stillwater River Publications, [2022]
Identifiers: ISBN: 978-1-958217-40-5 | LCCN: 2022914547
Subjects: LCSH: Homeless persons--Fiction. | Poverty--Fiction. |
    Recovering alcoholics--Fiction. | Redemption--Fiction. | Self-
    esteem--Fiction. | Male friendship--Fiction.
Classification: LCC: PS3603.A86842 J64 2022 | DDC: 813/.6--dc23

1 2 3 4 5 6 7 8 9 10
Written by Stephen B. Casserly.
Cover illustration by Elisha Gillette.
Interior book design by Matthew St. Jean.
Published by Stillwater River Publications,
Pawtucket, RI, USA.

JOHN

I

The shrill scream laced with terror pulled me out of a drunken, uneasy sleep. I was bedded down in a weed yard in an industrial area trying to sleep off my latest alcohol binge. I rolled to one side quickly in case danger was imminent. Through the air thick with a misty rain, I became aware of the location of the scream. It was dark but I spotted three figures about eighty yards away. They were in an isolated area between two abandoned industrial buildings. There was some muted light from spotlights on the buildings.

Two of the figures had a third held down who was still scream-ing. I watched while the two repeatedly punched and kicked the one that was down. I stood up and checked my condition. My head was pounding but seemed manageable. My balance was off but I knew it would quickly get better with movement. I started walking toward the three figures.

Walking brought me a little clarity. As I got closer, I could make out the nasty intent of the two assailants who held the third down. Rage welled up me in when I saw them beat him repeatedly to get their way. I picked up a stone and threw it hard in their direction. It hit one of them in the leg. I had his attention. He let his friend know they had company. The friend had his pants half pulled down and quickly pulled them back up. They turned towards me and braced for trouble. They were in their early twenties and big. The third person was younger and smaller and was moaning on the ground half naked. He had been about to be raped.

The one who had had his pants down was enraged. He squared off with me and said, "Fuck off or I'll seriously hurt you."

I looked at him calmly, knowing his malevolent evening had run its course. My silence seemed to anger him more. He came at me fast and swung hard, missing my jaw by inches. With his body off balance, I stepped in and smashed the side of his neck with my fist. He dropped to the ground. The second kid came charging at me full tilt. When he was close, I kicked him hard, catching him full in the solar plexus with my foot. I knew he'd be out for a bit, and I turned my attention back to the first kid who was mouthing obscenities and death threats with a raspy voice due to my punch. He had stood up and I came at him, dodging a slower swing than his first and hitting him hard with a three punch combination. It put him on the ground with his leg in an awkward position over an old timber, which I took advantage of by jumping on it, thinking it would probably break. I was right. He screamed in pain looking and sounding shocked.

I had the impression these two were tough and quick enough to take on most even or lopsided situations. The second kid who I had kicked in the solar plexus was just now catching his breath, but he was still on the ground. He was eyeing me warily with a combination of rage and fear. He wasn't the leader, but I felt the need to put the fear of God in him. I walked over to him slowly and, with a quickness that surprised him, kicked him hard in the stomach. I then punched him viciously in the face twice while he was lying on the ground groaning.

I turned my attention back to the guy with the broken leg who was screaming obscenities and death threats at me as fast as he could. I had to admire his nerve in threatening someone who had just beaten him so. I wasn't sure if the pain was motivating his screams at me.

I walked up close to him and looked him in the eye. He became quiet and stared back at me. I was startled. He had an evil look in his eyes. With a broken leg and having gotten hit hard a number of times, he was showing a toughness that almost matched his meanness. This left me with the difficult decision of what to do with him. Wistfully I thought this was a bit much for a man with a hangover. I used my anger to start beating him methodically. Just as I decided that he needed to die and was going to make that happen, I was grabbed by the third kid who had been beaten and almost violated. He looked at me and shook his head as if he knew my intention. After one last punch, I surprised myself by complying.

I looked at this kid who seemed to be about thirteen or fourteen years of age. He had pulled himself together a little but had some nasty welts and bruises.

"Do you have any broken bones?" I asked.

"No, I don't think so," he answered.

"Do you want to press charges against these two?"

He just slowly shook his head. I thought about that for the moment.

"That probably means you're on the run from a foster home you don't like or a group home."

He looked away and didn't say anything, confirming my guess. I considered if there was something else I could do for the kid. I came up blank.

I looked at the tough guys lying on the ground. One was out cold and the other was moaning audibly. I knew the kid would be safe from them. At least for some time. I was done here.

I walked back to my spot in the weed yard. I found my sleeping bag and backpack where I had left it. I rolled up my sleeping bag, grabbed my backpack, and was startled to see the kid who had been beaten standing ten feet from me. He had gotten closer than I ever would've imagined someone could get without me being aware of it.

Nobody crept up on me when I was conscious. The way I lived personal space awareness was a survival trait of the highest order.

The kid stated he wanted to go with me. I flat out told him he couldn't. There were dozens of reasons that request was absurd, but I was tired and hungover and headachy and really pissed off. Plus, I had to find another spot to sleep, so I let my demeanor say all that and started walking.

2

I was also in need of some alcohol. I checked my pocket and felt the small roll of bills I had there. There was a liquor store nearby I knew would still be open at this hour. I headed towards it.

I went through a mental check list of the city I was in, gauging the possible dangerous spots I needed to keep in mind. I thought of a route to a sleeping area that I could take after I hit the liquor store.

In front of the liquor store, I stopped and counted my money. I didn't have enough for booze and cigarettes. It was either or. I felt like I had to have some alcohol in me, so I opted for the booze. I hated the thought of waking up hungover without a butt, knowing I'd really need a nicotine fix.

I started walking into the store when I sensed someone near me. It was the kid I had saved from a beating. He looked up at me and held out his hand. He had a roll of bills and seemed to be offering them to me. I asked him where he had gotten the money and he said he had taken it from the two guys I had beaten.

"You went back and rifled their pockets for cash?" I asked.

He nodded. I wondered why I hadn't thought of that and nodded grudging respect for his action.

"You will need money if you're staying out on the street," I said.

He took the money, jammed it in my jacket pocket, and quickly moved away. I started to say something but figured, what's the use. I pulled out his roll and counted it. It was over one hundred dollars. I looked up and he wasn't anywhere to be seen.

I thought, *The hell with it.* I went in the liquor store and splurged on a quart of Jack Daniels and a pack of Marlboros. Vices in hand, I started heading to some woods I knew of maybe a mile or so away. I wanted much less of a chance that I would be disturbed in the sleeping off of my next hangover.

This is what I had come to. Living on the streets and looking for places in the woods or weed yards to sleep off drinking binges. I briefly considered getting back to the AA meetings that had kept me sober for some years. I quickly dismissed the thought knowing I wasn't ready. I also wondered, not for the first time, if I would be dead long before I got ready. I was progressively getting worse, a phrase I had heard many times at meetings. I was living out the nightmare scenario that I had been promised. Lucky me. Enough with the musings I thought. I needed to commune with my friend. I opened the bottle of Jack and took a swig. It was good. I had been maintaining on cheap alcohol due to my lack of funds. I was going to enjoy this bottle.

I was forty-three years old and had nothing but the clothes on my back, a sleeping bag, and a few possessions in a backpack. I had grown up in Boston with drunken parents and alcoholic insanity all around me. The neglect, abandonment, and abuse I had experienced had made me an expert on running the streets to survive and becoming a fighter. My time on the streets growing up was marked with hundreds of street fights, fights over anything and everything. Marking turf, pissing contests, slights, it didn't matter; I had fought over it all. I loved to fight.

I had been shamed and abused as a youngster and the feeling of not being able to move and protect myself left me when I started swinging my fists. Every fight gave me the chance of getting back at someone for the shame and powerlessness I had previously felt. I had unfortunately felt a lot. The tension, drama, and bullshit that preceded a fight became an addiction to me. The release for me came with the fight and I didn't care if I won or loss and even welcomed getting hurt so I could stoke my rage and feel something.

Eventually I got to a boxing gym and became skilled as well. I became a minor legend on the streets, being the crazy kid who wouldn't back down and was wildly good with his hands, known for having a vicious right cross that had ended many a fight.

Alcohol came into the picture, and I lost a boxing career. My fighting skills were always handy with my street life though. Trouble never seemed far away.

3

I thought about the kid that had given me the money. Money had been hard to come by of late. Temporarily I felt relieved of money pressure, and it made me grateful. I'm sure he was grateful for being rescued from the kids who had beaten him, but I hadn't expected anything from it. I hoped he would find his way and be okay.

I found the path at the edge of the woods that I had been looking for. It led into a wooded area that would be good for camping overnight. I could even make a fire if I could find some dry wood around. I found my penlight to use in the darkness. There was still a mist falling which made the darkness seem eerie as I moved away from streetlights and other neighborhood lighting. I found a small clearing about a half mile in and found some twigs and branches that were dry under some leaves. I started a small fire and started looking around for some good deadfall wood that I could use to get my fire going.

I heard a sound and turned toward it quickly. It was the kid again. I stayed quiet to see if anyone else was nearby. I heard and sensed nothing. I looked at him hard for a long moment. I sensed no ill intent or subterfuge coming from him. "You've pulled off the unbelievable hat trick of sneaking up on me three times," I told him. I couldn't remember anybody who had ever done that even once when I was conscious. I asked him why he was there, and he asked if he could stay the night in the woods with me.

"Nowhere else to go tonight?" He nodded and I thought what the hell. "Find me some dry wood and help me make a fire," I told him.

He quickly scampered around and found some more wood to add to my pile and soon we had a pretty good fire going. I made camp near the fire and checked the perimeter of the woods. I liked this spot. It felt far enough from civilization that the chances of being disturbed were small.

I asked him how he had come to be with the two guys who had beaten him. He told me they were known predators and all the local street kids tried to steer clear of them. He told me they had really messed up a fifteen-year-old boy, who ended up in the hospital for a week after they raped and beat him. This had occurred several months ago, and nobody had seen them for a bit, thinking that maybe they had left the area. "They had appeared out of nowhere when they grabbed me," he said. He got really quiet and serious for a moment and said, "Thanks for saving me."

"No problem, kid," I told him.

He got quiet and looked a little nervous. He said, "My name is John." I contemplated that and realized he didn't want to be called "kid." He was asking for a modicum of respect. After what he had just been through, I didn't have any problem with that.

Looking at him I realized this was a huge ask for him and a bigger risk. At this stage I could easily tell him to fuck off and yet he had asked anyway.

"John," I asked, "how is it that you came to be living on the streets?"

He looked happy I had complied with his indistinct request to use his name and not call him "kid" and began to tell me.

"My parents were both alcoholics. My father use to beat my mother and then he would beat me."

"Where are your parents now?" I asked.

"My father is still in prison. He got charged and convicted after that last violent rampage."

"How about your ma?"

"My ma continued drinking and that is why I was put in state custody. I'm not sure where she is but she may be staying at my aunt's."

"How old were you when all this went down?"

"I was nine."

"How old are you now?"

"I just turned fifteen."

Six years since he was removed. Now he was a runaway from whatever placement the state had him in.

"That's a lot of trouble to have to deal with in anyone's life, never mind someone as young as you. I'm sorry your life turned out so hard."

He got quiet and looked away. After a moment he said, "That's the first time I really felt listened to when I told my story."

My God, I thought. If that was true, it was sad beyond description. It was also poignantly painful.

He got quiet again and I got busy with my bottle. I lit up a cigarette, laid back on my backpack, and tried to relax. A bone-weary tiredness crept through me. The booze was enabling me to relax, and the relaxation was putting me to sleep. John started to talk again, and I nodded a couple of times like I was listening. In short order I was down for the evening. It took John fifteen minutes or so to realize that.

4

The morning was glaringly bright at daybreak. At least that's how it seemed to me. My hangover probably negated me being a good judge of that, but the mist and clouds of the previous evening had lifted. I looked around. I was alone. John was gone and had left my blanket neatly folded on the ground where he had slept, or where I assume he had slept. I recalled some of our conversation of the previous evening and wondered if I'd see him again. I had a feeling that shocked me. I missed him. I wished he was still here. But I knew the last thing I needed was some kid tagging along with me with my lifestyle so I quickly dismissed the thought.

I pondered my next move. I was thinking I should leave this city after last night's incident. The guys I had beaten might tell the authorities about me which would mean I could be picked up and detained and who knows, charged and convicted. I also thought about the evil one; I had really hurt him. He could be in a coma or dead for all I knew. Moving on might be the wise move.

I had a little money thanks to John, and I considered neighboring cities. I had been using the railroads to travel from city to city when a move was indicated. Freight trains still crisscrossed the country and, if I was careful, I could usually get on board one undetected. I had several options for nearby cities. Soup kitchens, liquor stores, and safe woods to sleep in nearby were major considerations. Also, who I knew in the cities. With my deteriorating condition, I really didn't want to see anyone, but it was nice to know I had that option if I felt desperate for some reason.

I thought about that and realized I hadn't looked anybody up in over a year. I had been to a number of cities where I knew people but hadn't gotten close to finding anyone. I was isolating more and more. The ease and comfort with which I did this concerned me.

I thought, *If an alcoholic dies in the woods undetected does that mean he never existed?*

Way too deep a thought for this moment. I grabbed my backpack and set out for downtown and something to eat.

I found a diner that served breakfast. I was hungry but settled for an order of toast and coffee. Still hungover, I didn't want to tempt being nauseous all day by eating a full breakfast. I figured I'd get a full meal later in the day. After my second cup of coffee, I felt a little better and decided to move on. I paid my bill and started crossing the street. I was heading to a freight yard I could easily access about a mile away. I'd make my final decision on where to go from there.

On the other side of the street there were two young girls panhandling. Maybe fifteen years old or so. More street kids. As I started walking down the sidewalk towards them, two guys in suits walked by them and were asked for money. Words were exchanged between the suits and the girls. I didn't hear all the words, but I got the gist of the exchange. One of the suits, when he was almost abreast of me on the sidewalk, turned and told the girls they could suck his dick.

On an impulse I shoved him hard when he passed me. He stumbled for several feet and then fell. Enraged he jumped up and came at me swinging. I sidestepped his punch, grabbed him from behind, and twisted, locking his arm behind him. I turned him in a way where I could pinch a nerve on his neck, which was very painful. I walked him over to the two girls while holding him thusly and told him to apologize. I could see he was having a problem with the idea, so I applied pressure on the neck nerve to help him. His friend, the second suit, was hovering around, telling me I'd better let him go and other idle chatter. I ignored him. A final squeeze induced the apology I was looking for and he told the two girls he was sorry. You could see he really hated doing it. I started to let him go when the smaller of the two girls came over and kicked viciously, aiming for his crotch. He managed to block it with his leg just as I was letting him go. Free and out of pain he quickly walked away with his friend.

Undaunted the smaller girl looked at me and said, "Do you have any spare change?"

I thought, *You have to love the streets sometimes for the sheer survival drama.*

I considered the girl. She was short and wiry, pretty and tomboyish. She looked like she had been on the streets awhile and could use a shower, clean clothes, and a decent meal. She also looked very angry. Angry at society, angry at her circumstances, and angry at men would be my assessment. I sensed that she didn't know what to think of me.

I reached in my pocket, pulled out my short roll of bills, and held out two twenties for her. She looked at the bills and then back up at me in disbelief. I was about to tell her that there was no caveat connected with the money when the second girl moved forward, quickly grabbed the two bills, and said, "Thanks, mister." She was taller than the first girl and thinner still. Gaunt even. She had a strong accent and a soft voice. Eastern European or Russian probably.

We looked at each other for a long moment. She was opaque. She wasn't showing anything. She had left vulnerable behind a long time ago. I knew it covered a painful history. She held my gaze for another long moment. Without saying a thing, I let her know I saw her. Her eyes moved. I took it as a sign that she had heard what I hadn't said. I turned and moved on.

I immediately chastised myself for giving away half the money I owned in the world. My mind went on a field day about this. I knew only one way to get it to quiet down. I figured I had enough whiskey and money if need be to take good care of it when I got resettled for a bit. Whatever resettled meant at this point. Several strong drinks were usually needed to quiet the negative chatter.

I thought about the two young girls I had just met. Fourteen maybe fifteen years old, on the streets surviving. They were a good combo. The little one was tough and scrappy and ready to take anybody on. The taller one was cool and thoughtful and would temper the smaller girl's destructive anger. I liked their chances. I said a prayer that they would get off the streets before they got really hurt.

I wondered what kind of resources there were for runaway kids in this city. In some cities there were options that were acceptable to the kids.

I started mulling my alternatives for nearby cities and communities when I jumped three feet as a defensive action. Once more my seeming nemesis John had managed the unbelievable feat of sneaking up on me. I looked at him for a long moment, wondering if he worked hard at these ninja skills if his. Whether I was sober or hungover, nobody, and I mean nobody, snuck up on me. The streets were always predatory, and one had to constantly be on guard for thieves, gangs, and, of course, your occasional psychopath. I had had run-ins with all of the above and had my share of enemies. I could not recall a single instance of somebody getting in my safety zone without me knowing it. John had done it four times now.

He asked me where I was going, and I told him someplace where folks didn't sneak up on me. He asked me again if he could come with me. I figured he had earned an explanation. I told him I was a problem drinker and got drunk pretty much daily. I wasn't in any shape to be taking care or even considering someone else.

"Then there is the legality of it. Someone sees us living on the

streets and they will probably think I'm a predator. You're not at legal
age for three more years. You can get picked up anytime for being out
here."

He argued that if we got picked up, he would simply tell them we
had just met and he had tagged along against my will.

"Nothing will reflect back on you," he said. "I don't care if you're
a drunk. I don't have anyone else, and I just want to hang with you."

I stopped and looked at him for a long moment. He had really
been through the mill, and I could see and even feel it for a moment.
If I was his best option, that spoke volumes. I sighed deeply and told
him I was leaving town and I was really sorry but I couldn't let him
come with me.

There was nothing I could say that was going to make that easier,
so I turned and started walking.

5

When I got to the rail yard, it took about an hour to figure out which rail train was going where. I decided to hop one that would take me to another northeast city that wasn't too far but far enough to hopefully keep me safe from getting picked up for the "incident." I found a freight car with an unlocked door that was about half full of crates of some sort. Plenty of room for a few hour train ride. I closed the freight car door behind me and laid down using my sleeping bag as a pillow, pulled out my bottle of Jack Daniels, and took a few stiff swigs. I really needed that. I felt the buzz of all kinds of feelings in me and needed to numb that out. I had a lot to think about. I had experienced more drama in the past eighteen hours than I had in the previous six months. I thought about the chances of the police finding out about the violence from the previous night. I also thought about the panhandling girls and John. Especially John. I had more interactions and conversations with him than I had with anyone else in the past two years.

I awoke to the rhythm of the train slowing. I had fallen asleep before it started. Now it was dusk, and the train was stopping. John was sitting across from me, leaning against the other side of the car. He said hello. I looked at him for a long moment. I could see I wasn't going to lose him. I knew I could if I felt the need, but it required a cruelty that I didn't think was warranted. I made a decision to let this play out. I asked him, "Why am I not surprised to see you?"

He smiled, taking it as a sort of acceptance.

We got off the train when we felt it stop and quickly left the rail yard. We were in a city with a large park within it. I knew of some heavily wooded areas in that park and decided that's where we would bed down. First, I needed food and more alcohol for later. I headed for a cheap restaurant where the food was reasonably good. John, my shadow, was now in tow. He was uncharacteristically quiet. I was grateful for that.

I had money for tonight but not after. I debated ways to acquire some in the near future. Besides panhandling, I did on occasion work. I thought of several people I had worked for in the past in this city. I thought I might try to look them up tomorrow. I wondered if I could physically put in a day's work.

At the diner we sat in a booth and ordered food. John started talking. My state was such that it distracted me from a mild hangover. He started telling me about some of the group homes he had been in. Some of them had been okay and decent and others were abusive. He had run away from the last one because of constantly being criticized and accused of doing things he had not done. He felt like that he never got seen or heard and was blamed for having motives he didn't have and doing things he didn't do. I asked him how long he had been on the streets. He said one year. He told me it wasn't that bad once you got used to it. I considered asking what getting used to it entailed but decided we had conversed enough. I paid the bill, and we headed off to the park I knew about.

We set up camp in a thickly wooded area in the park. I was hoping we would be far enough removed in the woods from city predators. We lit a small fire, and I got down to a little serious drinking. I asked John if he had any friends on the street. He said mostly acquaintances, but he was pretty friendly with two girls in the city we had just left. He divulged, "You met them yesterday."

I noted that and asked him what he was talking about.

He told me they were the two girls I had run into and then had given money. He told me they had texted him asking him if he knew about a homeless guy that fit my description. I got a little uneasy thinking about how easy it was to be visible on the streets to God knows who. I got very uneasy when John told me they knew about me taking Fric and Frac, John's two predators, off the streets.

I started lecturing John about the need for plausible deniability especially when it came to violent incidents where someone got badly hurt. He explained to me that removing those two guys from the street was news of monumental importance to the runaway population. It needed to be broadcast. Everyone knew they had come back into town, and someone had put them in the hospital. He told me he had told his friends about the incident, but he would text them and tell them to be quiet about my identity.

"You're a rock star in their eyes," he said. "And they're pretty tight lipped about everything."

"Text them and make sure," I told him.

So much for street anonymity. Getting involved with John was complicating my simple low-profile life. I drank some bourbon to quiet the chatter in my head. Soon I felt better, cavalier even, as I got drunk. *Bring it on*, I thought. *Bring it on.*

The next morning broke with the light of a nice sunrise. Not that I noticed things like that anymore. I was hungover. A chronic morning condition for some time now. John was sitting by a tree reading a book. He had policed the area and cleaned up the remnants of the small fire we had going the previous night. I had told him that was how I traveled, not leaving environmental trash anywhere and leaving the area not worse off for having been there. He had heard me and followed through without further cajoling. I was gratified and let him know that.

When we got to the downtown area, I got coffee and decided to make a few calls to seek work. I didn't have a phone and was wondering if there were any phone booths in this town when John pulled a cell phone out of his pocket and handed it to me. I looked at him trying to recall an instance of saying or even implying I needed a phone. I came up with nothing.

I called several people I knew who I had done some work for in the past. I got ahold of one of them, but he didn't have any work. I decided to go and look up someone I had been friendly with in the past. I didn't have a phone number for him, but he used to live on the south side of the city which was about a mile and half walk. Tony was his name. Tony was a guy I had drank with and gone to AA meetings with. We weren't tight but he was about as close to a friend as I had in my life. On occasion I had helped him with some work projects. He was handy and often scored carpentry and home improvement projects.

Tony was an interesting character. He had a childhood full of neglect and abuse facilitated by a raging alcoholic father and a mentally ill mother. He started drinking and fighting back at life at the age of thirteen. He had done time in reform schools and prison. By the time he got sober and to AA, he was really beat up. Physically he had liver and kidney problems and also had the physical problems of a lifetime of abuse, beatings, and violence. Emotionally he was so shut down he had problems with what a feeling was. I was drawn to him when we met. What that said about me I had never considered. I thought of him as my type of guy.

We got friendly after an incident in a bar we were both in doing relapse drinking. Three guys were drunk and acting belligerent with everyone else in the bar. When they started bothering a woman friend of his, he let them know he wasn't having it. He had the look that made people back away but didn't have the skill to back it up if it came to that. This day it came to that.

One of the guys just belted him in the jaw and he went crashing into a table and on to the floor. The three of them started moving in for the kill when I got involved. I put all three on the floor with vicious punch combinations fueled with my rage in myself for having relapsed yet again. I then picked them up one by one and physically threw them out of the bar. I was hoping they had more fight in them but after getting hit hard they all folded quickly.

I thought, *What is the world coming to? If you're going to be a bully in a bar at least have the dignity to take a punch or three.*

When I came back in the bar, Tony had a beer and a shot in front of him and one in front of the bar stool next to him. I sat down and drained the shot. It was good whiskey and I sighed with appreciation. He signaled the bartender, and he poured me another. He looked at me with a bemused look. He emoted some through the look in his eyes, but his face never changed. It was like he had sat on a barstool for so many decades that his face had frozen. When, on rare occasion, he tried to smile, he looked uncomfortable and failed in his attempt. After I downed my second shot he said "You know, you're okay. You play your cards right I'll let you hang out with me."

His comment was so unexpected and out of character it actually made me laugh. Something I hadn't done in a long time. It felt good. It also broke my horrendous mood. I ordered another round from the bartender, and we sat and drank together like that for several hours. Not saying much, just drinking. At the end of the night, we were friends. Or as close to friends as either of us got in this life. I had run into him once after that and done some work with him on another occasion.

Every time I thought of Tony, I remembered his cavalier attitude in the face of the vicious beating he narrowly avoided. Before, during, and after he acted like it didn't matter if he got stomped on that night or not. I interfered but he seemed okay with whatever way it went. What will be will be was his attitude. Amazing, especially because he knew what a vicious beating was like. He'd had a number of them in the past.

The more I thought it about the more disturbed I felt. If he didn't care that much, did that mean he had cancer or something that he wasn't talking about? Or did he live on a day-to-day basis with that much ambiguity about pain and life itself? The attitude scared me because it was how I felt. I often didn't care one way or another no matter what happened. It was something one developed living a drunk's life on the street. Especially over time when the defeats, chaos, violence, and constant negativity took its toll. I knew at times I was in danger, and it made me worry about Tony.

I became anxious to find him and find out if he was still okay. People I could relate to and almost call friends were a rare thing in my world. When we got to the house he lived in, I knocked on his front door to no avail. I found him in a garage behind the house tinkering on an old BMW motorcycle. To my relief he still looked okay. He looked like Tony.

After talking some, I discovered he had gotten sober again and had nine months of sobriety. He had found several meetings he liked and a counselor he felt comfortable with. He said he didn't really care for talking about his life but when he could he admitted it seemed to help. I told him I was happy he was doing good and looked well. He still had the same frozen expression on his face but looked almost healthy. Healthy for him; a relative term.

A mild euphoric feeling swept through me finding him in good health. I repressed the feeling of happiness and relief that he was okay and doing well. He tried one of his weird smiles and then suppressed the feelings he had about me.

We stood there for a moment staring at the BMW motorcycle until we had our emotions under control. I knew somehow that this was wrong but couldn't express it, see it, or find a different way. Quietly staring at the same BMW motorcycle for a long moment was the only way we could intimate care. It wasn't a great way to show emotion but it's what we had.

He looked at John quizzically and I gave him a brief synopsis of how we came to be. We caught up a little on news. Mainly a litany of people who had died or were still doing okay in sobriety.

After a bit I got down to asking him if he had any work now or coming up soon where he could use a hand. He said he had a job where he could use a laborer for a couple of days. I told him I could use the money and opportunity for work. I arranged to meet him there early the next day. He offered his couch, but the weather was warm and mild, and I knew a good place to camp not far away, and I also had John in tow, so I passed.

We passed a good diner on the way to a wooded area we would camp in. I pointed it out to John and told him I might send him there to get food later. We found a nice spot to camp, and I decided I needed to rest some if I was working all day tomorrow. The sun was still out, and I leaned against my backpack and fell asleep with the warmth of the sun on me.

When I awoke it was dark, and John was sitting in front of a small fire he had made. He offered to get food and I agreed, gave him money, and sent him off. To my surprise I fell asleep again and came to with John shaking me slightly. We ate and watched the fire for a while.

I asked John a few specific questions about one of his group homes and he started talking about the system he lived in. Some of the group homes and people that worked there were okay in his eyes. Not perfect but okay. Many of the counselors and workers would not let him talk freely and when he felt that attitude he would comply and clam up.

I prodded here and there to see if he had bonded with anyone in his travels between group homes, counselors, and foster care situations. I couldn't find anyone. He liked questions but they would send him off on another round of stories and descriptions of things that had happened. It was clear the system had not been easy or good for John. I needed patience and energy to listen for a while. I had that but would then nod off after a time. John didn't seem to mind that and would even talk a while after he noticed me nodding off.

The following day I met Tony early in the morning with John in tow. I explained to Tony he would be an extra pair of hands and would be cheap. Tony was good with that. He was redoing a kitchen and bathroom in a house and needed laborers to haul demo material out a back door and around front to a dumpster. He appreciated having laborers so he could focus on exactly what he would need for the remodel. The day passed quickly. I guided and encouraged John while he worked. He wasn't experienced but had a willingness to help that was refreshing.

I found my endurance had dropped some from the last time I had labored. Despite that Tony was quite pleased with our work at the end of the day. He had plans the next few evenings which was fine and John and I headed back to our camp. I stocked up on some beer, not wanting to get so hungover that I couldn't work.

The next few days passed quickly. I got in a routine of working, eating, drinking beer, and sleeping. The work was dull and boring but necessary. I let John fill in the gap between what I expected of myself and what I could still do. Actually, my expectations were impossible for superman to hit never mind myself. Tony, however, was quite happy with the production he was getting from us.

John was in the habit of disappearing for an hour sometimes after work. That was okay with me because I wanted a quiet hour after work, if not a short nap. After that we would walk to a restaurant or diner to get something to eat. I would buy some beer and cigarettes after that as needed. We would then retreat to our little campground, start a small fire, and talk for a while before I nodded off.

A week passed quickly like this. I was acquiring a small stash of

cash that might last longer than two or three days. That felt gratifying. I was thankful for the work and discipline I needed to get there
and work a full day.

John would get talkative at night. He was opening up more and
telling me some really personal stories. Mostly of abuse and beatings.
I let him talk and then sometimes he would weep quietly for a bit.
Wisely I resisted the impulse to say something and would simply sit
with him. He seemed to appreciate that.

There were other times when he would tell me about something
from his life and would then wonder or ask me if it was normal. I told
him I wasn't sure if I was the right person to ask about normal, but I
knew it was a far cry from a healthy loving family situation. I let him
know that it really sucked getting bounced around from one fucked
up situation to the next and having indifference and apathy by care-
givers be the best he would end up with.

At times listening to John got way too close to home and I would
drink more and zone out from the pain. I wasn't really aware of what
or why I was doing that, but I was. One time John opened up about
his mother. He felt betrayed and abandoned by her because she kept
drinking and was unable to keep him out of the state system. He told
me some really painful and poignant stories about his ma and how
fiercely she would fight to get her booze. I knew she was powerless
but those weren't the moments to tell John. He needed to get in touch
with his anger and pain. He would start out angrily telling me a story
until the pain hit. This time he stayed angry and talking while he
cried. At least for a bit. Then he sobbed for some time. Deep, painful
sounding sobs. I had drunk enough to get by my inhibitions and went
over and simply put my arm around his shoulders. We sat like that for
some time until he cried himself out. It took quite a while.

I couldn't tell you why or how, but I knew that from then on, no
matter what happened to either of us individually, John and I would
always be connected.

6

We continued to work for Tony. He booked several more jobs and continued to need help at least on a part time basis. It was a chance to get a small bankroll and to have a little stability for a while which felt good.

John and I fell into a routine of sorts. He would work with us most days unless he really wasn't needed or he had a mysterious personal thing to do.

We had moved our camp to a more advantageous and secluded spot. He would sometimes disappear in the early evening and then show back up. He would say he was trying to stay in touch with friends. Some in person and some by phone, text, and email. He was always concerned about his phone and phone plan and access to the internet. Runaways now had cell phones and were internet savvy.

I started thinking on how John should be in school and what he was missing out on education wise. We would talk about that. He felt he didn't learn much in school because the kids were so wild the teachers spent most of their days trying to keep discipline so they could teach.

John had figured he would get his GED degree in a few years and then go to a cheap community college that he knew about. He would learn then. That was his plan. He also couldn't go to school if he wasn't in placement, and he definitely didn't want to go back to his living situation.

I thought he had a decent plan in place as far as getting an education but didn't tell him that. I knew his life was one of the streets at the moment. That meant uncertainty, danger, fighting to eat and stay safe. It wasn't conducive to higher learning. I liked the fact that he always had a book to read in his downtime. That was a habit I had developed, and it had paid dividends in knowing and understanding things. I wanted to see John get a stable environment so he could get a real education.

I checked myself. I realized that I was thinking of John like he would be in my life from now on. The truth was he could be gone in an instant. The police on a routine stop could send him back to his group home, and that was in another city. He may run away again and try to find me, but I was transient too. I moved around a lot and liked doing it alone until recently. It came to me. The thought I had been avoiding. The one thing I swore I wouldn't let happen again. I had gotten close to someone, and they had gotten close to me. It made me feel vulnerable. Because I was. Fuck.

Time to do some serious drinking. Putting these thoughts and feelings together made me realize I hadn't been drinking enough to keep them at bay. I had cut way back on my drinking to show up every day for Tony. It was the dance I did off and on with booze. Crossing and uncrossing the line of heavy drinking to maintenance drinking. It was something I did when I needed to work or to get somewhere and I wanted to actually get to my intended destination. It was not something I always had control of but had done well of late so I could work with Tony.

This night I crossed back over the line into heavy drinking. I got hammered. It felt good for a bit until it didn't. I got dizzy and semi-nauseous and then passed out. I came to in the morning with a vicious hangover. I still had some bourbon and drank a bit to keep the jitters and horrors at bay. It was late and after my usual work time. John was nowhere to be seen. I wondered if he had gone on and worked with Tony. I was too drunk or hungover or both to be able to work this day. That suited me fine because I felt overdue for a bender. Three weeks of being responsible without getting hammered was my outer limits of controlled drinking. I gave myself up to the bottle. I blacked out soon thereafter.

I woke up out of my hangover and blackout a day and half later. John was sitting nearby watching me. He looked scared. I rummaged in my backpack for some pain killers I had for my headache. I popped two of them and looked for some water. John handed me a bottle of water and I drank it in five or six swigs. I knew how thirsty and dehydrated a heavy bender would make me. I had a certain checklist of things I would try to do to get back to the living. Painkillers and water were a start.

After a bit, I focused back in on John, who was still there watching me, looking scared. Now the bewilderment and horror started. What had I done in the blackout? Looking at John made me think it wasn't good. I got up and walked into the woods to relieve myself. I took a roundabout route back to camp trying to dredge up a memory of the last forty-eight hours. I came up blank and felt uncertainty and doubt when looking at John. I had had his respect and was afraid I had now lost it.

I got angry remembering my initial warning to him about how I was a drunk and I didn't want responsibility for another or for my behavior when drinking in front of another. Too late. Too late in the not caring about what another thought. I cared about John and what he thought of me. I hadn't wanted to be in that position. I hated caring, I hated feeling, and I fucking loathed feeling vulnerable.

I also always hated the torture of waiting to find out what I had done in a blackout. I either had to drag it out of someone who had

witnessed my antics or suffer the repeated declarations of how crazy I
had been with no details. John fell into the former category of witness
with the dragging out process. I would need to wait until he decided
to talk or start haranguing him for details.

Fuck it all. I rummaged around for some alcohol and found a bottle
of bourbon with enough left to take the edge off. I took several long
swigs and then found my cigarettes. I lit one up, sat down against my
backpack, and closed my eyes. I tried to distract myself until John
was ready. My mind was all over the place like it usually was after a
bender. I took another long swig out of the bottle and calmed myself
a little. Then I waited. While waiting I started planning my next
alcohol run and where and how much I could get.

While deep into my next binge planning, John asked me if I remembered the previous night. I came back to the present and regarded
him. Thinking this didn't look good I told him I didn't remember a
fucking thing, and if he was going to enlighten me of my activities of
the night before, could he do so quickly so as not to make me think I
had killed someone.

He proceeded to tell me how Tony had come to our campsite and
tried talking to me and after insulting him I had hit him and called
him terrible names until he finally left. This hit me hard. I had no
recollection of seeing Tony since the last time I had worked with him
which was now four days ago. I questioned John and found out he
continued to work for Tony while I drank. He had told Tony how
much I was drinking and how crazy I was acting, and Tony had come
here last night to see what he could do. As was the case with most
drunks, he couldn't do much but get insulted and frustrated.

I had been particularly nasty in my behavior with Tony. Terrific.
One of the few people in the world I cared about. He'd probably get
over it in time, but now I didn't want to deal with it. I wanted to
drink more. Another bridge burned.

I was disgusted with myself, with others, and with everything, and I wanted to drink really bad, but I didn't want to think about anything or be here for even a moment longer. I soldiered through my hangover and quickly packed up. When I was done John asked me where I was going. I ignored the question and walked off. The truth was I didn't know where I was going. I just knew I didn't want to be here. Instinctively I headed for the rail yards. I figured I would jump on the next train and figure out the rest later. Still flush with my work money I stopped for a couple of bottles of decent whiskey and a carton of cigarettes. I would need them. I was going on quite a run.

7

All I could hear were birds chirping when I woke. I was face down with my arms scrunched under me in an uncomfortable position. I stretched my arms while keeping my eyes closed. I felt sick as a dog and knew I had a horrendous hangover. I was afraid to open my eyes. It was way too painful to have to deal with anything. Eventually it got more painful to not deal with whatever came next.

I opened my eyes. I was surrounded by woods and that was good. I loathed coming to in public places. I slowly started moving and sat up after a time. Everything worked. So far so good. The woods started to look familiar. It was the wooded area I had moved to after I first met John. I tried to remember coming here to no avail. I searched for my last memory. I sensed something out of place as I got up. It was the figure leaning against the tree twenty feet away. It was John.

He was watching me intently. I didn't see or sense anyone else. I rummaged for my painkillers. Then I looked for water. John pointed to the ground near me where I found a bottle of water. I sat down and tried breathing slowly to slow my heart rate. I drank the water and tried calculating how long I'd be in severe pain this time. I felt nauseous, dizzy, and had a pounding headache that could turn into a migraine. I needed a drink. I looked around for a bottle with something left in it. John came over and handed me a bottle of Jack Daniels with five or six good belts left in it. Enough to nurse me back to the living if I handled it correctly. I took a few good belts and waited.

I went back to trying to find my last memory. Nothing. Nothing from the decision to leave the city where Tony was. The last thing I remembered was stopping at a liquor store to stock up. I wondered how much time had gone by. I had the feeling I had been in a multiple day blackout. I checked my backpack. It had my stuff in it. I checked my money. Gone. I rifled my pockets and found some crumpled up bills. I had spent my stash. Not a good sign. I laid down on the ground and closed my eyes and tried to think as little as possible. The headaches with my hangovers had gotten vicious. I had the beginning of a migraine and when I got one, they would incapacitate me for some time. I was hoping to avoid that.

I stayed like that for some time breathing slow, deep breaths, pushing thoughts out of my mind as best I could. After twenty minutes I could feel my heart rate slow down and my mind calm a little. After thirty minutes I sat up. I nursed the few remaining sips of whiskey for over an hour occasionally taking slow deep breaths in order to lower my heart rate and facilitate calmness.

After an hour it came to me that John and I had yet to exchange a word. He had given me several bottles of water and the remaining whiskey. He sat quietly by the tree, alternately watching me and reading a book. He hadn't complained or accused me of anything. It was like he was simply taking care of me, no questions asked. The silence truly was golden, with me being in my condition, and really appreciated. The friendship and feelings of care I felt towards John made me uncomfortable. I pushed them out of my mind. I became aware I was really hungry and needed to eat.

John came over and asked me if I could make it to the diner about a mile away. Now he's psychic I thought. I answered yes and started walking down the path that led out of the woods. John fell in next to me and we walked in silence.

We ordered our meals and ate them in silence. When we were finished, John picked up the check and paid the cashier. We then headed back to our campground.

When we got there, I smoked a couple of cigarettes and got in touch with how exhausted I was. I laid down and was starting to fall asleep when I thought of something. I hadn't thanked John. I sat up and found John reading again near the tree. We looked at each other for a long moment, at the end of which I said, "Thanks," and laid down and went to sleep.

8

I came to about twelve hours later. I felt better and like there was hope for me to return to the living. I was alone and took my time getting up. There was a Dunkin Donuts coffee cup nearby, and when I picked it up, I found that it was still warm and filled with coffee. John must have left it for me. The shot of caffeine was heavenly. I drank the coffee, smoked several cigarettes, and laid down again. I was still recovering from a vicious bender and needed to continue to rest. I napped off and on all day while trying to get my bearings back. I still didn't know what day it was and how long a bender and blackout I had been on. I wished John would return so I could ask what he knew about my latest escapade.

Try as I might not to, I had to think about my drinking. It was getting worse. It was something I had to consider. Whereas it always nagged and bothered me, it was now seeming to often scream at me for attention. I used to be able to mellow out the nagging with a few drinks but now had to get very drunk to shut out all the voices. My blackouts were becoming more frequent and more unpredictable. I didn't remember coming back to this city. That was always scary and on occasion terrifying.

Blackouts opened up a Pandora's box of possible terrifying

scenarios. I had been in serious fights during a blackout with no recollection of the fight. This fact alone made me fear really hurting or
killing someone and coming to in a jail with no recollection. Waking
up in a city or place other than where I thought I was like I had here
was also more than a little unnerving. With my experience of things
that did happen in my blackouts and my imagination running wild
with what could have happened, a single blackout could fuel terror
for months. Multiple day blackouts ramped up the terror and fueled
nightmares. I was starting to have multiple day blackouts every
month. It felt like I had no control.

I thought about going to an AA meeting. I was starting to feel
desperate. I was thinking of my past forays into program when I had
had some success. Going back after being out and drunk for so long
seemed like an insurmountable task. I knew many had done it but
that didn't make it seem any easier.

Enough. I needed food. I gathered myself together and headed
into town to eat. I went to the diner that I frequented when I was
in this area. I ordered a meal and ate with an appetite not decimated
from an ocean of alcohol. I was also hungry because on benders I
tended not to eat and would go days with just the calories from the
booze I was drinking. I barely had enough money to pay my bill and
decided to take a walk while I considered my next move. It was early
evening, and the weather was quite nice.

I was in a pensive mood. I wondered where John was, what I had
done in my last blackout, and where I could make some money. These
questions and wondering how much longer I could continue drinking
began to take a toll on my tenuous good feeling.

I came upon John in a small park in the center of the downtown
area. He was talking to two young women. When I drew close, I saw
it was the same two I had run into and given some money. I remembered John had said he was friends with them.

The smaller one looked at me so suspiciously that I almost laughed.

My handout apparently hadn't garnered me any goodwill with her. The other taller girl just watched me with no change of expression. I remembered now: she was opaque and didn't show anything.

John introduced me to them. Then told me their names were Cora and Ekaterina. Cora was the shorter one and Ekaterina was the tall one with the strong accent. I had heard John reference them as the kitten and the raccoon. Cora had a kitten in her hand, so I surmised that was why with her. I made a mental note to ask why raccoon with Ekaterina later.

Cora looked at me and said that she had heard I had a problem with alcohol also. I looked at her without saying anything. I was pissed. I didn't care for John talking to them about my drinking. John spoke up saying that Cora and Ekaterina both were going to AA meetings because they thought they had a problem. I looked at John then back at the girls and asked them if it helped. Cora spoke, saying it did but that she had some reservations about the program. I resisted the impulse to ask about those reservations, not wanting this discussion here and now.

I looked at John and asked if he was coming back to camp later. He said he was. I turned and walked away. I made a beeline back to camp. I hated any of my business being made public. The thought of John talking about me bothered me to no end. Enough that I thought of cutting him loose over it. When I calmed myself a little, I considered that may be a tad drastic and that the first step would be to talk to John about it. Back in camp I realized I was dying for a drink but was trying to resist. I had little money and didn't want to go back into a blackout if I did start drinking. This last blackout had scared me and was still fresh enough in my mind to make a difference.

My musings were interrupted by John who came running into camp trying to tell me something.

When he caught his breath, he said his friends were in danger and needed our help. With no more explanation he started running back the way he came.

I started following him but couldn't keep up. John was running flat-out. I had to stop and catch my breath several times, but we quickly covered the ground back to the same park I had met him in earlier.

When I got there, I caught the beginning of a melee. There were seven or eight kids surrounding John's two friends. There was also a small crowd of kids forming on the periphery watching the action. There was a lot of yelling going back in forth between the two girls and the crowd of mostly male teenagers. One kid was trying to wrestle something out of Ekaterina's hand. I watched John jump in, trying to help her, and get hit hard and knocked on his ass. He immediately jumped back up and started helping again.

This time another kid hit him hard, and he fell again. Five of them then surrounded him, stomping and kicking him viciously while the others started hitting the girls. I lost it and went into action.

I ran into the crowd swinging and punching hard. I tried to make every punch count. I avoided most of the counter punches thrown my way. If I could hit someone hard, unless they had experience being hit like that, I could count on them being out of the fight. Several minutes in, I was standing in the middle of a dispersed crowd. Some had moved away from the fight after being hit. Many were lying on the ground moaning and holding on to some part of their anatomy.

I saw Cora and Ekaterina looking at me with their mouths open. They also looked scared. I went up to them and asked if they were alright. They nodded yes and I quickly looked them over for damage they might not be aware of. Cora had the beginning of what looked like a black eye. She didn't seem to realize it yet, so I considered it not too serious. John joined us and I checked him over thoroughly. I had seen him get punched and kicked multiple times. He was smiling and moving okay but I knew he'd hurt later on. He was still running on the adrenaline the fight produced.

I asked the three of them what this was all about. Cora answered saying, "Ekaterina and I have some history with this group of guys and when they saw her iPhone, they started demanding it."

I made a mental note for a better explanation later on. I took inventory of the crowd and sensed no threat left. There were a couple of kids who were trying to check on their friends lying on the ground, but they had no interest in continuing anything. I started to hear sirens in the background and knew it was my cue to leave. I told John I wanted no part of the police. He nodded his head understanding.

I walked away quickly and from a hidden vantage point I watched the police arrive and start questioning people. I noticed that John and his friends had left also. I took a circuitous route back to camp. When I got there, I found John already there with Cora and Ekaterina. I looked at John, and apparently, he could read my mind. He started telling me how they needed a safe spot for one night, but tomorrow they were going back into placement. Also, how careful they had been to make sure no one had followed them here.

I was angry about him bringing his friends but decided to let it go for the moment. I told the three of them not to stray far tonight or get an impulse to run into town for an hour. I told them the police might be looking for all of us. I thought the police would be looking for me. I figured that the people I attacked would blame me for any fighting that had occurred. I had just got here and had to leave. I'd be at the train tracks in the morning looking to board a train out. The fight had left too many variables with too many people. Somebody or several people would finger me and say I instigated the whole thing. I felt I had no choice; I had to leave.

I asked Cora and Ekaterina what had started the melee. Cora said, "The boys were getting a little too mouthy, so I told them to fuck off. They got angry at that and then they wanted to look at Ekaterina's iPhone, which would have disappeared had she let it go. We have a little history with several of those boys because we turned them down for romance or sex. Now every time they see us, they harass the shit out of us. After I told one of them to go fuck himself, pushing and shoving commenced and someone hit me, so I threw several punches, and it blew up from there. Next thing I knew John was being stomped on and then you came tearing through the crowd."

It sounded typical of how things happened on the street. Something small could morph into a major fight or incident. Then everybody would say someone else started it.

"I am glad you are both alright. Serious damage can be done during brawls with long-term health consequences."

They started talking amongst themselves and I got lost in my own reverie. I felt anger rising and a strong desire for a smoke and a drink. I had one cigarette left and started feeling aggravated about my lack of funds, need for a drink, the fight I was just in, the crowd around my campfire, and the fact I would need cigarettes soon and didn't have any, when John came up to me and handed me a bag with a pack of cigarettes in it and a handful of vodka nips. Not enough nips to get drunk but enough to take the edge off. I looked at him for a moment and he shrugged, walked away, and sat back down next to his friends near the fire. With one fell swoop he cut my raging off at its knees. It was almost disappointing. I was grateful, however, for the cigs and nips. And once again I wondered why John seemed so psychic.

I lit a cigarette and sat down on one end of the small campfire John had going. I cracked open and downed one of the nips he had given me. It tasted so good I opened and downed two more.

John asked me if I remembered the fight.

"Sort of," I replied. "I remember punching the kid that I saw kick you when you were on the ground. After that, things happened quickly, and my instincts kicked in."

Minutes passed as I was reflecting on the fight. I looked up and caught Cora and Ekaterina watching me.

I asked, "What?"

Cora started and said, "You were very effective with your punching. Most of the kids went down after one punch."

"Like a superhero, coming in and saving the day," Ekaterina added.

Cora jumped back in with, "I've seen all kinds of fights on the street, but I've never seen anything like that before."

After a moment Ekaterina said, "I was definitely expecting a beating before you jumped in. Thank you."

"A fuckity fuck type of beating for sure would have been had without you there," she continued. "Yes, we definitely could've gotten really fucked up."

I got a kick out of listening to these two girls talk and finish or add to each other's thoughts. And the use of profanity was almost an art form.

"Ekaterina, how important is your iPhone, seeing how it played a major role in this melee?" I asked.

"This is the latest iPhone, and it is my lifeline to the world. There is no way I would give this up without a fight. I had actually had it ripped out of my hands during the struggle. I had to get it back from the guy who took it from me. When you punched him, he dropped it, and I grabbed it. If you hadn't shown up, I don't know what I would do."

She picked up the phone and showed me. She beamed happiness as she showed me her phone. *A fucking phone*, I thought. I lightened up, remembering all the stupid reasons I had gotten into vicious fights in the past. At least the phone was worth a lot of money.

I told them I had experience being in fights where I was outnumbered. "Most street kids weren't fighters or at least not the way I had been growing up. If you hit them hard, the shock of that will break their will and the fight becomes less lopsided. If I can take out a number of them early on, I can win the fight," I explained.

I was surprised that I had told them that. Talking about fighting or anything really wasn't my typical M.O. I felt like I wanted to give them an explanation. I felt close to them for a moment. It wasn't a common feeling for me. I omitted the rage I felt when I saw one kid kicking John when he was on the ground. I had taken him down with a brutal three punch combination. That detail fortunately got lost in the melee.

The three of them broke into an animated conversation among themselves about the day's events. They were still high on adrenaline. I listened in for a few moments and realized how tired I was. I laid down and quickly fell asleep.

The following day broke cloudy and cool. Good traveling weather I thought. Upon awakening I made a decision on where I was going. I felt tired and confused and like I was hanging with too many people. I needed a break from the streets, and I was headed to a city where I'd hope I would get that. Somewhere where I could get a respite from the streets. It was a bit of a long shot, but I was willing to take it. I was going to a city where an old girlfriend lived. I would try to stay with her for a short time.

John and his friends were just starting to wake when I was about to leave. John asked where I was going, and I told him to the rail yards. He knew what that meant. He looked torn or confused about whether to stay with his friends or travel with me. I nodded and headed out with my backpack.

It was the world-goes-to-work hour which is what I called the period between 7:30 a.m. and 8:30 a.m. A ton of anxious traffic on the road and a lot of pedestrians in cities. It was a time where, try as I might not to, I always judged the hell out of myself for not having a job and being part of the whole scene. Then I would think back on lost opportunities and chances I walked and drank away from. Then I would think about the girl I missed and would've had a family with if I hadn't blown that. Then I thought about the fact that all my possessions were in my backpack, and I had all of thirty-seven dollars to my name. Then I would find a thousand different things, reasons, and proof that I was the biggest loser in the history of mankind.

All the judging and thinking would be an automatic thing that happened so quickly and unconsciously that it actually felt natural. It wasn't. On rare occasion I would see it. I would realize I had a brutal thought pattern toward myself. But now I had only one solution to deal with it. I downed my last two nips I had from John and made a beeline to a liquor store so I would have sustenance on my travels and I could keep my sanity.

9

I woke up to the familiar clacking sounds of the rails and slight sway-ing of the car. John was asleep across from me with his head on his backpack, scrunched up against the side of the car. I studied him for a moment. I thought he would stay with his friends, so I was mildly surprised. I had grown fond of him beyond anything I thought I was even capable of. It felt awkward and uncomfortable. He had pierced my heavy armor by just being. I pondered if my chances of staying with my ex- girlfriend were diminished if John was with me. I guess I'd find out.

When we got to the new city, I made a beeline for a phone booth I used to know of. Halfway there with John in tow, I realized John had a cellphone. I asked for his phone and told him I had to make a private call. I walked a little distance and called Celeste.

Celeste was a woman I had been involved with some time ago. She seemed to love me despite my drinking and general loser status. She gave me carte blanche to call her, but I was always expecting her to tell me to go pound sand and tell me to get lost. Even when I was drinking hard, she wanted me to stay with her, but I couldn't let myself take advantage of her like that. On several occasions I had called her to get off the streets for a brief time. The sex and the good food she cooked were added motivations for me. I considered the last time I had spoken with her and was shocked when I realized three years had gone by without me calling her.

I took a deep breath and dialed her number. She answered. When she realized it was me, she went off on a rant.

"Are you kidding me? It's been three years since I've heard from you. You can't make a call once a year to let me know you're alive?" There was a long pause. "I'm seeing someone and he's here now. Let me guess," she continued, "you were hoping to come crash and stay with me for a bit."

"Yes," I answered.

"You're a real piece of work, even considering that I'd let you stay with me. You have some kind of chutzpah," she added. "Apparently you haven't changed one bit."

There was another long pause. I gave it my best shot and asked, "How long?"

She came back with, "Give me an hour," then hung up.

I gave her two. I realized this could have gone the other way and felt grateful while suppressing the thought I may cause more harm or pain showing up and leaving yet again. A debate started raging in my mind about how much of an asshole I was for going to stay with her again.

When we got to her house, I told John to give me an hour and then come by and I would have an answer for him on whether he could stay also. I didn't want to walk in cold with John in tow. I felt an explanation was in order first before she met him.

It felt good to see her despite my underlying guilt. She looked good and I told her so. Always pretty, she looked relaxed and like she was taking good care of herself. We chatted and caught up on what some of her siblings were up to. She had several troubled brothers she was always trying to help out. One was in prison for a drunken brawl he had been involved in where one of the participants had gotten badly hurt. Another was scrambling for housing and had just spent two weeks living with her after losing his job. He had lost his job due to his drinking. She was a classic enabler who felt responsible for getting family members out of trouble even if they caused it.

One of the reasons I felt I couldn't stay with her long term was that once more she would be enabling somebody: me. For some reason that bothered me to no end. She had said on numerous occasions in the past I could stay with her, but I just couldn't. Instead, I lived on the streets while occasionally taking a street vacation by staying with her for a week or two. Apparently, I hadn't had a vacation in three years.

I got around to telling her about John. She asked me where he was now, and I told her he would be nearby shortly. She told me to make sure I got him there and that she was a little surprised about my being involved with another person in this way. I told her no one was more surprised than me. Celeste knew what a loner I was and that I valued my isolation.

After an hour I took a walk to find John. He was waiting patiently at the end of the street. I brought him back to Celeste's house and introduced him to her. I left him alone with her while I took advantage of being able to take a shower and shave. I knew she would know everything about John and me since we met by the time I finished cleaning up but I was okay with that.

Celeste was putting together a meal and talking to John while in the kitchen when I came out of the bathroom. I watched them for a few seconds before I walked into the kitchen. I could see they were already becoming fast friends. I figured that would happen but not in the first half hour. When I walked in the kitchen, Celeste told me John had filled her in with all the blanks of our joint adventures. John looked a little embarrassed about her statement, but I nodded at him and said, "I'm glad," letting him know she was okay to talk to.

Celeste whipped up a quick dinner which I found wonderful in its simplicity and taste. John and I made short work of our share, and she refilled our plates. Home cooked food was a luxury when you're living on the streets, and John and I relished the meal.

After dinner, we chatted for a while and then Celeste showed John a den on one side of the house where the television was. She came back to the kitchen and gave me a look. I got up and followed her into the bedroom. When we got there, she closed the door. It took me an hour to relax but everything worked well after that. I was extremely gratified to know that. Drinking, smoking, and living on the streets all could lead to some performance problems. It hadn't yet.

After the sex, Celeste had that angelic look women get if they come really well or multiple times. Anytime I had ever seen that look the only word that came to mind was angelic. Not satisfied, or sensual, or peaceful but angelic. For the umpteenth time I mused on that. I realized I had never told a woman that and wondered if I should. Maybe, I decided but not tonight.

The sex also made me relax and let go and shortly after, I was sleeping. I slept through the evening and awakened with a start the next morning. Upon realizing where I was and in a bed with nice sheets I stretched for a minute and fell asleep again. I came to around 11:00 a.m. I had slept essentially fourteen hours.

I got up, threw on some clothes, and meandered to the kitchen. John was sitting there drinking coffee and reading a book. He informed me that Celeste had gone off to work and we had the house to ourselves.

Being in and existing in a house felt strange to me. Her house was very quiet. I felt unnerved being in a dwelling without the sounds of nature around me. After several coffees, I found her TV and had John find me the remote and a news channel. Shortly after I decided to take a walk and check out her neighborhood. I found a market about a half mile from her home and bought some groceries. I walked back to the house and made myself a sandwich. John had found some programs he liked and was watching them intently. I talked to John about keeping Celeste's house clean and the way we found it and he gave me a look. A look implying that was obvious. I nodded and went off to take a nap. Sleeping in a bed was a luxury I hadn't had of late, and it felt good. I slept another two hours.

When I awoke, I still felt tired and realized a couple of things: Being in a safe environment was allowing me to relax in a way I usually couldn't do; my body felt spent from the constant anxiety, drunkenness, and hangovers I usually had; and I felt like I could sleep for several days straight.

Celeste had returned from work and was in the kitchen with John making dinner. I had wanted to make dinner, but I had napped too long. I was thinking about the booze I had bought along with the groceries when Celeste handed me a glass of bourbon with ice in it. It was her bourbon, and it was good. Celeste didn't drink like me, but she could on occasion drink too much. We had several drinks before dinner and continued drinking after. Within several hours we were both pretty drunk.

Celeste started asking some very direct questions about what I had been up to. John had caught her up on our shared history and she asked things like about where John was going to end up when he eventually got picked up and how would I react to that. She also wanted to know what was up with the incident with Tony and if had I talked to him since our blowup. Then she asked about my health and if had I seen a doctor and mentioned that I looked a lot more stressed and had aged some since the last time I had seen her.

"Thanks for sharing," I said. Then I chuckled and told her living on the streets really got you in the moment because there was no good projection from the life I was living, and I worked hard at not pondering such things because it was too painful. I also drank those questions away. It was the nature of the beast.

She took in my answers and looked sad and hurt for a moment.

She told me it really pained her to see me and yet she wanted to see me despite it. I started feeling regretful about coming here when she finished with, "but I'm glad you came."

I was starting to ponder that when she made us both another drink, came over, sat on the couch next to me, and put her head on my shoulder. For a moment, I felt confused until she made it very clear that I was not persona non grata and took me to her bedroom. I had a moment of panic that I had drank too much but when things heated up, I turned out fine. I shortly realized how much I missed sex and the corresponding intimacy. We were more relaxed after our first encounter and got sexual the way we used to back when I first had been involved with her. It turned out very good for both of us.

After, she allowed me to light up a cigarette and ended up having one with me. Shortly thereafter I was out. I woke up the next morning alone with the sun shining in the window in a way that made it clear it was far from sunrise. I figured Celeste had gotten up and had gone off to work.

I found John in the den watching some show on TV. I sat and watched with him for a little while. I pondered my next move, and I came up blank. I wasn't sure how long I would be welcome here, but I thought for the moment I'd take it a day at a time.

I asked John if he liked Celeste and he answered with a profound, "Yes." He got quiet for a moment and then said she was nicer than any of the foster mothers he had been placed with over the years. After another moment he added; "She also seems wiser than any of the counselors I've seen."

He stayed quiet after that comment, watching TV, but when I glanced over at him, he had tears streaming down his face. I was surprised and taken aback by that. I sat there frozen while I thought about his tears. I figured he was displaying emotion that was probably in a normal range for people, but I was clueless on what to say or do. I sat there and watched TV with him.

Later on, I walked the neighborhood again to get out and get some fresh air. It felt good to exercise but the relaxation I had been feeling left me wanting to keep it short. I returned to the house and made myself and John some lunch. After eating and cleaning up we ended up in front of the TV again. John had been unusually quiet during lunch. After a time, he simply said, "You're an idiot for not staying with Celeste." His eyes never left the screen.

I thought about a response, I thought about an explanation, but in the end, after a time, I said, "Yes, I think I am." In a few minutes, I fell asleep.

10

We got into a bit of a routine at Celeste's. Celeste would go to work, and John and I would have the house to ourselves. Celeste would come home, and I would help her make dinner. After dinner, Celeste and I would drink her bourbon. We would either talk in the kitchen or watch television with John. Celeste had a few shows she had to watch, and John always had opinions on what we should watch at other times. Apparently, he had done some serious TV watching in the past and was very opinionated on TV series.

Sometime in the evening, Celeste would set off for her bedroom and I would join her there. Living on the streets had left me with an almost nonexistent sex life. Rediscovering it and the intimacy after was a wonderful thing. The fact that Celeste thought I was good in bed didn't hurt either. I'm sure it had something to do with why I was there in the first place.

I had met Celeste when I had stopped for a nightcap in a bar that she happened to be drinking in. I had struck up a conversation with her by raising my glass and saying, "Here's looking at you, kid." I had thought the line a bit lame, but it turned out it was her favorite line from her favorite movie. She loved Bogart and all his movies but especially *Casablanca*. An hour later, we were tearing through her sheets, riding a wave of lust fueled by alcohol and compatibility.

We were involved for a year after that. We had a lot of good times, but my drinking accelerated near the end of it. It was turning into a problem for her. She was willing to put up with me, but I left after a bad fight when I realized I couldn't stop my drinking and my brutal, rageful hangovers.

Shortly thereafter I lost my job and started my descent to the streets. This was the third time I had taken a vacation from the streets with Celeste. My instinct was it may be my last.

After several days at Celeste's, John and I began doing things around the house and in the yard while she was at work. We edged all her shrub and flower beds, weeded her gardens, and bought a few bags of fresh mulch and flowers that were on sale to help spruce her landscape up. John was a good worker. He caught on quick and was good at being assertive in following through. Which was helpful as I would lose my energy after a bit. I would let him know what needed to be done and then let him do it.

During the fifth day of being at Celeste's the doorbell rang and there was a guy at the front door. I opened the door and asked him what he wanted. He looked at me accusingly saying, "This isn't your house."

Again I asked him what he wanted.

"Where is Celeste?" he asked.

I simply said, "She isn't here now."

I knew for sure now that this was the guy Celeste had been seeing before I showed up. He was angry and resentful about me being there and wasn't trying to hide it. When I told him Celeste wasn't here, he said she didn't like strangers in her house. I had empathy for the guy and thought about explaining how close Celeste and I were in the past. I thought about telling him I wouldn't be here long, or perhaps about the strange twists and turns in life.

I felt the futility of trying to explain anything and ended up saying, "And yet here I am."

He didn't have anything to say after that and simply left.

I had a bad feeling about him showing up and figured this situation wasn't going to last. Frankly I didn't blame him for being upset, and it wasn't like I had long term plans to stay with Celeste.

Apparently, he was good friends with Carl, one of Celeste's brothers. Carl showed up the following day demanding to know what was going on. He remembered me but didn't care for me and John being there. I remembered him and his propensity when not drunk to come over and act protective of Celeste's life. Sooner or later he'd drink, get in a jam, and need Celeste to bail him out. Now he was in the sober protective phase. I tried to talk reasonably with him but didn't seem like I was making headway. I had a feeling that he had been drafted by the new beau and no doubt there was something in it for Carl.

He asked about John in a way that made me think he would happily drop a dime to have him picked up by the authorities if he found out his true circumstances. When Celeste came home, we talked about it. She had never been able to detach from her brothers, whom were all younger and problem drinkers and probably alcoholics. Sooner or later one of them would be in a jam and she would bail them out or help them somehow. She confirmed what I had suspected. Her new guy was very friendly with Carl. She told me she liked him but was not yet committed to him although he would like her to be. Her new beau and Carl had become friendly when he had bailed Carl out of one of his jams.

Celeste thought that Carl would be a problem soon considering his propensity for binge drinking. He could come by and start a beef with me or even get John involved somehow.

It was time to move on. If I wasn't staying or trying to make it permanent with Celeste I had to leave. I didn't want to cause her more grief. I felt like I had caused her enough trouble just by showing up. I told her what I felt. I apologized for showing up and disrupting things. She said she didn't care, and she was happy I came. She told me she really liked John and asked if I had any long-term plans with him. I told her I didn't, and she impressed on me how much he looked up to me.

She told me I'd have difficulty parting from him and that I had some responsibility with him. I thought about that for a moment and realized she was right. Despite working hard at not having any responsibility I had managed to create some. I pushed the thought away vowing to deal with that later.

That night together would be our last. We had dinner and went to bed early. The sex felt poignant. We both knew it would be the last time. In the morning, I got up early and got my few possessions and John ready for travel. I waited for Celeste to get ready for work. I hugged her for a last time and neither of us wanted to let go. She started weeping silently as I hugged her. If I could cry, I would have. After several long minutes, she said, "Go and don't come back." She then walked out, got into her car, and drove off.

It was finished. I stood there for a moment, letting the feelings sweep over me. I felt alone and empty in a way I had never felt before. It became too painful to keep feeling. Time to move.

I picked up my backpack, nodded at John, who had been waiting discreetly nearby, and started walking. On the way to the train yard, I stopped and bought a bottle of bourbon. It would take some serious drinking to deal with this.

I I

We ended up back in the city where Tony lived. We were camping in a wooded area near where we had camped before on our last visit. I went on a three-day bender and spent three more coming down and trying to get myself decent. John was around every time I came to. Usually, he'd be reading a book or texting on his phone. He kept the campfire going during the chilly evenings and acquired food when we needed it.

Coming down and getting straight was getting harder and harder. It was taking longer and longer and felt more painful. The nausea, the headaches, and the hangovers were taking their toll on me.

I spent a week after coming down just nursing myself back to a state where I felt I could join the living. I ate, rested a lot, and went for long walks in the woods. I also accrued a couple of nights of good sleep. When I was straight, I decided to visit Tony and apologize for abandoning him and whatever else I had done on the bender during my last visit. This had been on my mind since I had left after the incident. Tony was a good guy, and I didn't want to leave an open sore between us.

I thought about my drinking on the way to his house. If I worked for him again, I couldn't guarantee I wouldn't abandon him again. I was unreliable, period. I had a problem with alcohol and that was that. I still didn't feel ready to quit. I felt I was in no man's land. I saw no solution on the horizon to my drinking dilemma, so I pushed the thought of it out of my mind.

I arrived at his house just when he was returning home from a job. He invited me in and got me a soda to drink while he cleaned up. When he came back, he had some iced tea for himself and sat down and lit up a cigarette. We regarded each other for a long moment.

Finally, I said, "What can I say? I'm an asshole."

He shook his head with a wry smile and said, "Yeah, when you're drunk you certainly can be." Then he looked at me seriously and simply said, "Well, are you ready now?"

I told him, "No, but I was edging towards getting ready."

Ready meant surrendering, and the whole idea was still anathema to me. On some level it didn't make any sense and went against my upbringing. Fucked up as my upbringing was.

I asked him if he had any work; he told me no, but he had already used John for several part time days and could use him for another week or so. I looked surprised.

"He didn't tell you?"

"No, he didn't."

I knew the answer, but I had to ask, "Why no work for me?"

He just looked at me for a long moment and finally I just nodded.

I heard a few of the details of my last blackout and still had enough humanity to feel embarrassed by some of the things I had said to him. I apologized and left. He didn't give me a lot of grief or continue lecturing about sobriety.

Like I said he was a good guy. He was also smart. I thought things over on the way back to camp. I considered going to an AA meeting. I knew unless I firmly committed to going to one, I would not get there. Firmly committing to one was beyond me at this moment. I thought soon but not now.

Initially I was a bit angry with John for not telling me he had hooked up with Tony again. After thinking about it I realized I was always either drunk or hungover and he had shown some nice initiative. He went to work while I was drunk or hungover. I felt proud of him for that and made a mental note to let him know that in the near future. It also meant we had a little money. We needed it, for I was getting low again.

When I got back to camp, John was reading a book. I asked him what he was reading, and it was an old Stephen King novel he had gotten somewhere for free.

We sat in the sun and discussed novelists and some of the things he had read. His reading had been quite extensive. He had read some of Stephen King, but he wasn't a huge fan despite liking them. J.K. Rowling's Harry Potter series was also read but with that turning out to not be a favorite also. I questioned him on that and found out he liked dramatic novels, novels about real life, historical novels, police novels, novels about crime. I told him if we got back to the city where we had met, I would take him to a great used bookstore where they had all kinds of books. He looked excited at the prospect.

Night was coming and we decided to get some food. We ate at a diner we frequented and bought some snacks and food at a market nearby on the way back. I bought cigarettes and passed reluctantly on buying booze. I had drunk light the past week and I thought I might get through a night without a drink, but I was worried.

When we got back to camp, we made a fire and talked. I gave John some suggestions on novels and told him he needed to read other books to try to figure out what he liked. He liked the idea and wrote down all the suggested books I had told him about.

I came to the realization John was pretty smart which made me ponder avenues of education for him. He had his plan for a GED and then possible local junior colleges. I started thinking I'd like him to aim higher than that. Or think about what he could do or read or study now that could help give him a leg up. Maybe online studying? I realized I was in over my head now because I was so old school and out of the loop of technology options. But then again, learning was learning and a book was a book, however you read it. I made a mental note to look up a friend who had gotten a lot of education after she got sober. Her name was Julie and she had quite a story.

Julie had run the gauntlet of hell with an alcohol, cocaine, heroin, and crack addiction. She had run the streets hard for years before she got clean and sober. I hoped she was still on the right side of sobriety because once she had gotten clean, she became a woman who wanted to be educated and she chased that as hard as her sobriety. I had picked up and left the meetings and had fallen out of touch with her as one does when they drink.

Well look at me, I thought, thinking of other people beside myself.

I laughed inwardly at my own joke, and John asked me, "What are you smiling about?"

I playfully put him in a headlock and told him I didn't think that was any of his business and asked him if he liked living. When he asked why, I told him the alternative could be arranged. He pushed me away and we pretended to fight for a bit.

When he got tired, he said, "You're a bucket head," and went back to the campfire and his book.

I sat down by the campfire and smoked a couple of cigarettes. I really liked John now. I had a terrifying thought about how vulnerable that made me. I loathed the feeling of vulnerability and caring. The equation in my head was that vulnerability meant pain. It was a position I swore I'd never be in. At least not again in this lifetime. It was a conundrum. One I wasn't going to solve this evening. Thinking such light thoughts, I drifted off to sleep.

Several weeks passed uneventfully. John worked with Tony for six to eight hours a day and then made his way back to camp. We would buy food and snacks and I would buy booze every second or third night. I was trying not to drink daily and to drink light a couple of times a week. My body needed a break from the alcohol and hangovers.

One day, trying not to drink, I took a walk in the city to distract myself. I was starting to feel a little better physically simply by not drinking every day. I wondered if I could handle that feeling and smiled inwardly at my own perception. I soon realized that the question of being able to handle it was valid. The thought came that I was addicted to pain as much as I was to alcohol. Feeling good and healthy would be difficult. This realization was startling as well as disturbing.

I had a sudden craving to be around people. The only way I knew how was in a bar. I found one I had frequented before that wasn't too much of a dive. I went in and ordered a beer. At times when I got lonely, I liked to be around people. I didn't necessarily want to interact with them, but I guess it made me feel like I was part of a bigger picture or something.

The bar was dark and had a jukebox playing something surprisingly good. I took that as an omen that this was where I was supposed to be. I drank my beer, telling myself that I'd have a few and move on. It was fifty/fifty. Half of me believed myself as the other half said "right" in a very sarcastic manner.

After a few beers, I felt a nice mellow buzz, the likes of which I hadn't felt in some time. Loosened up but not drunk. The type of feeling that used to be common for me and had gotten me addicted to alcohol. I hoped the feeling would last awhile as I was enjoying the music and the feeling that I wasn't alone in the world even if it was an illusion.

After drinking for an hour some people started coming in. It was 4:45 and an after-work crowd started filtering in. A woman who had come in and sat two seats down was asking me something which brought me down from my reverie of fantasies I indulged in while drinking at times.

She repeated her question of, "Do I know you?"

I regarded her for a moment, thinking she did look familiar. I racked my brain and the only thing I could think of was that I had been to some AA meetings in this area. I glanced at the glass she had in front of her at the bar and thought it looked like a bourbon. Having noticed my glance, she flat out asked me if I was a friend of Bill's.

"I have been but apparently not lately."

She smiled sadly at my reply and, after a moment, said, "I've known quite a few friends of Bill."

She didn't explain that any further which made me believe that she was referencing the program, as was I. After that reply, the conversation flowed.

It turned out her name was Sue and she worked for the state in the department of children and families. She had a supervisory position and had to make judgement calls constantly on kids' safety. Which kids were at risk and whether or not to put them in state care all with limited resources. Limited both in workers to check on the kids and in places to put them if they were at risk. To me that was the stuff of nightmares. I would second guess every decision I made and when some kid did get hurt or killed, I would simply fall apart.

She was okay with making those decisions and apparently did it well. I told her I was impressed with her ability to do that and how important I thought the work was. She seemed to really appreciate that. She had stopped by this place to take the edge off new budget cuts she had to deal with. In her opinion more budget cuts were making safety impossible for a large portion of the vulnerable.

I told her I thought it was the cost of doing business in this country now. Evermore pernicious with our vulnerable population. Like the restrictions on mental health if one didn't have insurance.

"Of course, everyone is up in arms about our weekly shootings in this country," I said. "It seems to me that if you boil any one of them down it comes down to a mental health issue. Without addressing that side, I truly doubt they will stop no matter what is done.

"When it comes to kids and runaways and throwaways, the predators are around in droves to take advantage of weakness, but society didn't want to bother allocating money for any service to help them," I continued.

I suddenly realized I had been on a rant, the likes of which I hadn't been on in some time. I focused back in on Sue, my drinking partner. She was listening to me with a serious expression. When I stopped, she looked a little disappointed.

"That was a very good overview of what I deal with on a one-to-one basis every day."

She asked me if I had been to college, and I told her I had taken a few courses in business many years ago. She got down to the question which for me was a little tricky. "What do you do for a living?"

I decided this conversation warranted the truth, so I told her I was a drunk living on the streets basically, but back in the day I had done this and that and what I could to get by.

She took a moment and mused on that, and then asked, "How is it you have such strong opinions on kids and mental health issues?"

"Probably because I'm living it and seeing it get played out on the streets day after day."

"And then you take one-on-one experience and extrapolate a picture of national scope." It sounded impressive when she put it like that.

"I guess it's how and what I think about between drinking sessions," I said.

We went on like this for a while. We both got a little drunk. It turned out she was single and was thinking what I started thinking. Perhaps impressed with the conversation enough to override her concerns with being with a homeless guy, she invited me back to her place.

When we got there, she told me she needed more stress relief than drinking would provide. I said, "I'm here to serve," with a pretty straight face.

The evening was memorable for good reasons, which was a nice change. The sex was passionate and free in a way I didn't usually feel until I had been with someone for a while.

My hangover in the morning was relatively mild which was good because I thought she didn't want me to stay alone in her place, having known me all of one evening. She got up early to get ready for work and when she left, I left with her.

We exchanged numbers with me giving her John's cell phone number with the caveat to tell John to tell me to call her. I got a quizzical look over that, but she was running late and had to go.

We hadn't talked much that morning but a bit of the glow from the previous evening warranted me a passionate kiss goodbye and a promise of future contact, both of which I was gratified to receive.

I headed back to the camp in the woods that I shared with John. I wondered if she would talk to her coworkers about the homeless guy she picked up at the bar the previous evening. Thinking about it got me depressed. I liked her and logic would tell her not to contact me. A homeless alcoholic living on the streets. The more I thought about it the more depressed I got. Then my thoughts went off on another tangent. *What's with all the people in my life all of a sudden? What am I, a frigging debutante?*

It was fucking John. Ever since I met him, I'd been dealing with people and relationships. Previous to him I had hardly spoken with anyone in three years never mind have sex. I pondered the connection of those two events the rest of the way back to camp.

I2

When I got back to camp John was sitting by a tree reading a book. When I asked him why he wasn't working with Tony, he ignored me. I walked over to where he was sitting and watched him. He continued to ignore me. This was behavior I had never seen from John before, and I sensed he was quite upset. I stood there and waited.

Minutes later he started with, "You're a bucket head you know. Where were you last night?" The intensity was a bit of a shock.

I told him what happened and that I had spent the night with a woman I had met.

"You're still a bucket head," he replied and pretended to read his book.

I sat down near him and thought about this. It took me three or four minutes, but it came to me he was worried about me. I blurted out, "Were you worried about me?"

"Nah, why would I worry about you?" he replied with sarcasm. "You never do anything unusual or illogical."

He had witnessed me insult and hit Tony in a blackout and then my corresponding remorse over the whole incident. He had also seen me drink almost nightly since we first met. The fact that he cared about me threw me for a loop. I had been on my own for so long I had forgotten or maybe had never known about having consideration for others in that way. It also touched me in a way that left me stunned for some time.

Eventually I simply said, "It hadn't been my intent to worry you. I never thought about it. I do get it now and next time I'll try to call you if something comes up like that. I'm sorry I worried you."

I realized I had just apologized for something. Apologizing about something or even having someone to apologize to was a rare occurrence in my life. It was memorable for its scarcity.

I grabbed my sleeping blanket and lied down. The drinking and extracurricular activities had tuckered me out. I also felt somewhat confused dealing with John's anger. I was wondering why I had apologized instead of telling him to go pound sand and get back to the group home he had run away from. Pondering such thoughts, I fell into a deep sleep despite the daytime hour and light.

When I woke up John was gone. It was late afternoon. I often catnapped during the day but couldn't recall sleeping solidly for hours. The sleep felt good and had refreshed me fairly well. I thought about the conversation with John I had before I fell asleep. It still felt confusing. When I got close to an emotional life I always felt messed up.

I felt restless and hungry and decided to head out to get something to eat. I went to a diner that was only about a mile walk. I had soup, a sandwich, and several cups of coffee. I figured if I ate well, I could resist the impulse to buy booze for the evening. I took a walk and headed to the downtown area that had some decent pedestrian walkways.

After walking for some time, I sensed someone staring at me. I looked up from my reverie and saw a group of women coming down the walkway in my direction. There were five women, and I scanned them quickly and found one of them looking at me. She looked familiar and I felt I knew her, but I wasn't placing her. She also was quite attractive and was well dressed in a business type outfit which was typical of the whole group.

When she came close to me, she yelled out my name and ran at me like she would hug me. Which she did. I was still trying to place her when she hugged me like we were long lost friends.

The synapse connected and I said, "Julie, I can't believe it's you." Which I couldn't. Always a pretty woman, I had never seen her looking so healthy and business glamorous. I thought she looked terrific. I told her so. She immediately came back with that it was in large part because of me. She then started telling her friends how I had set her on the path of sobriety after her last relapse. How I had always encouraged her to keep coming and that she would get it if not today then soon.

I remembered her going to a particular meeting that I went to and talking with her from time to time. I had no idea that it had meant so much to her or the particulars of our conversations. I did recall her bottom with the alcohol and drugs included her prostituting herself for money, which she was pretty hard on herself about. She had gotten sober young. I figured it was maybe seven or eight years ago now. This was the woman who had started chasing education with a vengeance after she had gotten sober. Apparently, it had paid off. She told me she was a lawyer and worked at the AG's office. Her companions were her coworkers. They had moved on with her promising to catch up.

She told me she had gotten her GED and then had enrolled in college. Financial aid, scholarships, grant money, and loans had financed it all. When she graduated from college, she had enrolled in law school. Upon graduation she had gotten the job at the Attorney General's office. She said she really liked being a lawyer. She had also gotten involved with doing some pro bono work for a juvenile justice organization. She considered that a way to give back.

I remembered her being attractive but always troubled and getting herself in jackpots. It was startling to see her look so healthy and animated. She had gotten sober and was still involved with the program and sponsored other women.

The conversation was good until she started asking about me. I told her the truth and didn't sugarcoat anything. She told me that made her sad because she considered me the primary reason she had gotten sober the last time and had got a life because of it. For the next thirty minutes she worked hard on convincing me to get sober again. It was both annoying and touching.

She would intersperse her pitch with these are the things I had taught her. She said I had convinced her that she was worth the pain of sobering up and that it was an easier road than drinking. She was particularly adamant about how I had helped her not to judge herself about the things she had done to keep herself in alcohol and drugs. Particularly about her prostituting herself. I had apparently told her she had no power over that and that was what the first step taught us. Either it meant what it said or it didn't. Powerless and powerless over all the things we did to continue the insanity.

I thought about if there was anyone else in the world I would listen to this long about the basics of getting sober. I couldn't think of anyone. There were a few people I respected and would listen to for a short time but not like this.

She began to get to me. She was taking bricks off the walls of my defenses. At the end of the thirty minutes the miracle occurred. I agreed to meet her at a meeting the following night. She gave me the address of the meeting and I promised I'd meet her there. I walked away with a confusing array of emotions and thoughts. The thoughts ranged from how annoying she was to was she an angel sent to rescue me. The feelings were more broad and harder to define.

One of them, however, was awe at the chance meeting with Julie and the phrase, "What goes around comes around." It also made me wonder if I had helped her eight years ago so she could save me down the road. Right here, right now was down the road.

I pondered these things as I walked awhile before heading back to camp. I felt a little dazed and confused from it all and felt I needed to walk to clear my mind. When I got back to camp John was there drinking a soda and reading a book. I realized I hadn't asked Julie about resources for college and online courses which I could have passed along to John. I made a mental note to do so the following night.

I sat and smoked cigarettes while I processed recent events. Having a one-night stand and then running into somebody that I knew well the next day was a lot of socializing for me. Then I was living on the streets and having to answer to John where I was the night before. What the fuck was going on?

Now I was committed to an AA meeting the following night to meet Julie. I thought about that and felt the creeping desire to back out of the meeting coming on. I dismissed it because I made a commitment to be there. Telling Julie I'd be there made it much harder to back out of.

My life felt like it was changing. I didn't feel like I had any control over it either. There wasn't really all that much going on, but I felt a need to control something or slow down all this socializing. I had been a hermit for some time. I had spent months on end in my head with the only human interaction taking place when I bought something.

I lived in a world of books and fantasies fueled by alcohol and hangovers. Bouts of serious lethargy and depression were common. There had been times when I moved as little as possible during the course of a day. Thinking about how I had been made me realize I really, really didn't want to go back to that mode of living. That left me with the alternative. Keep moving forward and accept the change and hope that it would be something better. I started to almost look forward to the AA meeting the following night.

I figured if I was going to AA and try and quit drinking again it made sense for me to drink a little tonight. I would buy a six pack after I went to the diner for something to eat.

I asked John if he was hungry and if he wanted to eat at the diner. He said "yes," and we started walking there.

He was unusually quiet, and I asked him if he was still mad at me. He said, "No."

After another moment I asked, "Then why so quiet and pensive?"

He said he'd talk about it at the diner.

Part of me wanted to whack him in the head and say, "Talk now." I would have these thoughts and impulses with John and just know that it was the wrong thing to do in that moment. At least I would know when I was sober or mildly inebriated.

My first impulse was always to try to control someone or something. It was familiar. It was how I grew up and had internalized to the nth degree. I also knew it was the wrong thing to say or do. I was beginning to realize how much I had hated it. Instinctively I knew John or anyone would also hate it so I was trying to temper my impulses to say or do something that reeked of control.

John was a boy soon to be a man no matter his circumstance. Despite my circumstance I was a big influence on him now. I needed to give him the space and respect that he deserved. The insight startled me for a moment. When did I start to get so introspective? I thought about it for a moment. The answer came. It was when a lot of things began to change. When I met John.

Meeting John seemed to have been a catalyst for many things to change in my life. I didn't know if I should thank him or hit him. I glanced over at him. I had become attached to John in a way I didn't think I was capable of. I had started to care, and the corresponding feelings of vulnerability and fear were getting hard to navigate. I would drink to manage those feelings. Then I would drink again to cover up those feelings of shame on what happened when I drank so much. It seemed timely that I was going to an AA meeting tomorrow.

It also felt like a possible relief to have a chance to stop drinking. It had become a lot of work to drink. The efforts to control, to drink reasonably, to not drink, were exhausting. Never mind recovering from the hangovers. Drinking when you were a problem drinker was a bitch.

We got to the diner, grabbed a booth, and ordered some food. John talked about working with Tony a bit. Tony was a good carpenter among other things. John really liked that he was learning carpentry and many other things from Tony. They had finished one job and Tony had scored another substantial job that would keep them busy for a couple of weeks anyway. The food came and we both got busy eating. After I ate, I ordered a coffee and waited. Patience was not a strong suit of mine, but I stayed quiet 'til John was ready to talk.

Soon he started. He had been talking with Tony and getting ideas. He found he wanted, was hoping for more from me. He had asked Tony if I got sober and had an apartment if I could be his guardian. Tony had told him it could happen, and John had run with the idea.

John said he'd like to live with me but in a better, more stable environment. He'd like for me to get an apartment. Then try to be his guardian. He said all this and then stared out the window like he was afraid to look at me. Which was wise because part of me was infuriated. I had told him when we met that I was a drunk and he couldn't expect anything from me. I considered reminding him of this but with my newly developed restraint I hesitated.

After a moment I considered reminding him that this was a foolish request. Then I thought he realized that and was asking anyway. John had courage. I had to give him that. Several times he had asked boldly for things that made him very vulnerable. This was one of those times. I could very well just tell him to take a hike.

Instead, I asked a serious question. "Why would you want me as your guardian?"

He said he liked the way I took an interest in what he did and what he was reading. Also, I would give him ideas for other good books to read. He told me he had never experienced anything like that before and he felt those were the types of things he thought a guardian ought to do. I took an interest in his education and apparently that meant the world to him. I also didn't talk down to him and that wasn't a frequent occurrence in his life.

I was taken aback by all this and sat silent for some time. Part of me was touched. Part of me was sad for it didn't seem like the little I had done should mean so much to John. Yet it had. Part of me was angry for several reasons. I hadn't wanted the responsibility of this kid, yet I ended up with it. The reason this made me angry was because it forced me to look at myself and my drinking. If I was sober and had confidence in my sobriety, I think I would take up his offer without hesitation. I really liked John and had grown close to him.

The thought of him leaving me would make me sad.

Startled I thought more about this. John had gotten in. He had gotten past my walls and defenses. Slowly and inexorably, he had broken through the lines.

Processing these thoughts, I had forgotten about John. I looked at him and realized he was quite anxiously waiting for a response from me.

I started telling John what an honor I felt it was that he would ask me to be his guardian. I told him I thought he was really honorable and brave and smart, and it was a privilege for me to get to know him so well. I told him I didn't know if I could get and stay sober. I wasn't totally closed to the idea but there was a lot that would have to happen before it was feasible. I then told him I had met an old friend who was a sober alcoholic and that I was going to meet her the next night at an AA meeting. Basically, I was going back to meetings to try and get sober again. He looked out the window for several long moments. He was silently crying. The surprising complement I had given him had touched him. It had also touched me because I was surprised I had come up with it. I found out later he was also emo-tional because he had been praying for me to get sober and I had just told him I was going back to meetings.

John knew the process and the power and need of meetings. I sur-mised he had been badgering the hell out of the usually uncommuni-cative Tony. Pestering him with questions until Tony had explained it to his satisfaction. I smiled inwardly at the picture of the two of them relating. I told John the bottom line was that we would have to take this idea like the program. One day at a time.

After this sober, deep, and intensely emotionally conversation, I asked John if I could borrow his phone. I called my new friend Susan who I had had a one-night stand with recently. I asked if she would meet me at the bar we had met in. I explained I was in need of some stress relief due to circumstances and jokingly reminded her how well I had taken care of her when she was in need. She chuckled and asked me if I remembered how to get to her place. I told her I did. She then asked how long. I told her half an hour. I asked her if I should bring booze. She said don't bother she had plenty but to get over here soon.

I handed the phone back to John and said I probably wouldn't be back to camp until morning. John looked a little disappointed, so I explained, "If you know you're going to try to get and stay sober the next day it made sense to do some farewell drinking."

I headed out and made good time to Susan's place. She was way ahead of me on the drinking, and I had to get physical immediately upon walking in her door. She started kissing me passionately and groping at my clothes. Minutes later I went down on her and in a surprisingly short time she had several strong orgasms. This gave me a chance to get some of her bourbon and get me ready for the next round. And like in boxing, it at least felt like there was only one minute between rounds.

The sex was wild, passionate, and intimate. It turned out we both needed a lot of stress relief.

The following morning, I woke up to the smell of coffee which I badly needed. I was hungover. Not the worst of hangovers but hungover none the less. I shuffled into the kitchen to get some coffee. Susan was in the bathroom, which was a relief because I definitely wasn't ready for talk, small or otherwise. Not before a couple of coffees anyway.

I sat on her couch and sipped the coffee and lit a cigarette. I was on my second cup of coffee when Sue came out of the bathroom. She went to the bedroom to get dressed which gave me another twenty minutes to rejoin the human race with pain pills and coffee.

I remembered I was meeting Julie at an AA meeting tonight. The brutal headache and hangover were a nice reminder of why I was going. This was far from my worst hangover, but I felt like my body just couldn't deal with any hangovers or drunken sprees anymore. Something that had been routine was now killing me. It would be a real relief to stop drinking.

Sue came out and got a fresh cup of coffee and sat near me. It was Saturday and she had the day off. She asked me why I had been so stressed. A conversation we had never gotten to the previous evening.

I told her I had met an old friend from AA who had talked me into going to a meeting tonight. I explained I thought I was ready to go back to AA and I probably needed a shove and an old friend had given it to me. I was tired of drinking and hangovers and my body couldn't take the abuse from alcohol anymore. Of course, that had left me in a panic for one last drink which she had provided along with the physical intimacy.

Sue was glad that I was going back to AA. She had heard some of my tales and thought getting sober would be a very good idea. She mentioned she thought about going back herself from time to time. She felt she wasn't ready. She had a hard time wrapping her mind around coming home from a hard day of work and not being able to drink. Her drinking felt manageable I thought. That would change if

she kept at it with the fervor she had shown me of late. *Time will tell,*
I mused.

Sue knew things would change somewhat if I did get sober and
she expressed a desire to stay friends. I was gratified that she wanted
to stay connected. I hoped it was possible. Time would tell on that
factor also.

I left and headed back to camp.

When I got back to camp, I found John reading a book. He didn't
have any work today. I sat down and smoked a cigarette. John asked
me if he would lose me over this woman I was seeing. I told him he
would not. I told him he would never lose me because of another
relationship, man or woman. I continued to smoke cigarettes as I
pondered why I had just said what I had just said.

13

That evening at 7:00 p.m., I walked the two miles to the meeting where I would meet Julie. I was a few minutes early and was greeted at the door by a young guy named Bob. I grabbed a coffee from the inexorable AA pot that was at most meetings. I found a seat and took a lay of the land.

It was hard to walk into an AA meeting after a long absence. Especially if you had been drinking. You felt shame and guilt and unacceptable and a host of other things that I didn't have the experience to describe. I also knew that if I stayed it would probably pass. I knew that if I hadn't committed to Julie to be here, I wouldn't have come.

Five minutes before the meeting, Julie arrived with a young girl in tow. I surmised she was probably one of the women she was sponsoring. She greeted most of the people she walked past with enthusiasm and a hug. Her energy was upbeat, positive, and infectious. She was the queen of the room, beaming with gratitude and positive energy. It was delightful to see. I had never seen her like this in the past, save for our recent meeting. When I had been sober before she had been the one struggling to stay clean and was usually pretty miserable about it all. She seemed like another person.

She smiled with delight when she saw me. I imagined she didn't think I'd show up. She introduced me to a couple of people sitting nearby that she knew. She credited me with being a big reason she got sober eight years ago. I was feeling bad enough about myself that it was nice to have anybody say anything positive about me. It also felt awkward. I didn't have any of her positive energy and I felt like a fraud for even being here. Mercifully, the meeting started without me having to talk or field too many questions. It was an open meeting where people from another group came in and basically told their stories. My mind was racing quite a bit, but I managed to tune in to a number of speakers for at least part of their shares.

Seeing Julie had made me truly happy for her. She looked terrific and was obviously well regarded by others. It had also sent me on an emotional tailspin. What the hell had I been doing and where could I be if I had stayed sober these past eight years? The loss of the years I could have spent sober felt crushing and unforgivable. More proof positive of what a loser and worthless person I was.

By the end of the meeting, I did get something I remembered from many other meetings. A modicum of hope. It was definitely tempered by the loss of a lot of time, but it was there. I felt like I was on a scale and the scale could go either way. Oblivion or sobriety. Both had their powerful attractions. After the meeting I told Julie I'd wait outside for her as she made her rounds.

I was on my second cigarette when she came out with her friend in tow. She questioned me on what I thought, and I told her honestly what was going on in my head. She listened and didn't go too overboard with her desire to give me what she had by continually talking.

After exhorting me to give the program another chance she caught the glaze in my eyes starting to form. She became quiet for a moment and told me how painful it was to be brought back to that terrible time when she was struggling so, and it seemed like oblivion could win over sobriety at any moment. She asked if I would go to another meeting, and I told her yes. She gave me a booklet with a list of meetings in the area and noted some that were close by to this area and particularly good most of the time. She also notated the ones she usually attended every week. Her next meeting was in two nights, and I told her I would meet her at that one. I told her I would consider others before that also. She gave me a big hug and I walked back to camp grateful for the time to process the torrents of stuff I felt.

That was the problem with not drinking; what do I do with the constant emotional discomfort? I always felt like I was in some sort of turmoil that only a drink would alleviate. As I thought that, I realized the solution to it. Meetings, lots of meetings. When I got back to camp, I found John reading a book with a small penlight he had. I knew he had another and asked to borrow it.

I started studying the AA meeting book to find daytime meetings as well as evening meetings close to me. I started to feel that if this was going to work, I would have to be a serious meeting attendee for a while. I made notes in the column of the book on some meetings I would check out. I had attended a few meetings in this area when I had been sober before, but this wasn't my home area then. I had met a few people but only vaguely remembered the meetings I had attended. I thought, *that fact might work in my favor*. I didn't want to run into a bunch of people who knew me from eight years ago. I would much rather start with a new area, set of meetings, and people.

14

After a month it happened. I stopped drinking. I had relapsed five times, but the drink was down, and I felt if I stayed on this path, I had a good shot of leaving it down. I had chased the meetings. Morning meetings, afternoon meetings, evening meetings; I had chased them all. I had found a person here and there that I felt okay to talk to. Not fully letting my guard down but a start was made. After consideration I had asked Julie to be my sponsor at least temporarily. She agreed and I had a person to really begin to talk to honestly. She encouraged me by constantly telling me she was honored to return the favor of help that I had given her eight years ago. I knew about her brutally hard times and circumstances, and somehow that made it easier for me to reveal my shit.

My five relapses had come in the first three weeks. During one of them I had called Sue on John's phone and spent another night with her. She had said she was surprised I had called so soon. I told her my relapse did have something to do with that. I explained that I was back at meetings but not quite there yet, "there" being having put the drink down for good. She gave encouragement for continuing until I got there. I thanked her for that and told her I'd try to stay in touch. We were comfortable with each other and both of us liked the other as a sex partner.

John had helped out in the last month also. He had his two friends Ekaterina and Cora come up and visit. They had gotten sober, and both had over four months clean. I spent time and went to meetings with them. Listening to them discuss the steps and many other topics made the process almost enjoyable. They had an interesting way of talking. Both of them were quite bright and had been together long enough that they often finished each other's sentences or embellished and continued each other's thoughts. It was fun to watch and listen to when they were in the zone of that process.

John had asked them to stop by the campsite and go to meetings with me for a few days when I was in my first two weeks. I was touched by the thoughtfulness this showed.

When they had arrived, I had questioned them about the melee we had been involved in. They told me that they had been questioned by the police and they had said some stranger had come and interfered when they were being abused and harassed by a gang of boys. They made it clear to the police that the stranger had saved them and was not the instigator of the melee. They also said they hadn't known me before the incident and hadn't seen me since.

They then told me how they had leveraged their rescue by me. Any time they had trouble they told the street kids they would get their new friend "The Avenger" involved. All the street kids had heard about the melee and knew what had happened. Unbeknownst to me, they also had all apparently heard about me helping John out and putting the two pedophiles in the hospital. Those two were known and feared by most of the street kids and it was now an urban tale of how I had saved John and beaten on both of them.

So on the one hand they had told the police they knew nothing about who I was while on the other, they told anyone that harassed them they would get their new friend involved if they didn't let them be.

I was uneasy about the fact that I might become identified. Dealing with the police could be a real hassle. Without funds for bail or lawyers I could do time over the most minor of things. This I knew from experience.

I understood and even admired the girls using what they could to stay safe. It was the code of the street. It was perception that mattered. After hearing about the melee, it made sense that they could summon me for retribution if someone crossed their line.

The fact that it wasn't true was trumped by the fact it could be true. Listening to Ekaterina and Cora tell stories of the street and stories of going to AA meetings and some of the characters they met was fun. Neither of them liked being sexually harassed, which is relatively commonplace on the streets. They would also interpret a lot of other more subtle behavior as harassment and break it down, describing what this statement or that statement actually meant.

It was not only fun, it was an education. Every time they broke down an instance of harassment, I recognized the truth in their description and analysis.

They stayed and camped near us while they were here. After several days they left with a program woman they had met who was giving them a ride back to their city. They were hustling money and had an arrangement with someone who had an apartment. They were renting a bedroom which got them off the street. They both attributed this step up to being clean and sober and not spending every dime on alcohol and drugs. They weren't of legal age yet being fifteen years old. They, too, had been like John and fled group homes and foster situations that they had hated. Although to be fair they seemed to have reached a point that they didn't want anyone telling them what to do. They wanted no restrictions and had opted for the streets over any rules.

Cora hustled money by writing and editing and coaching high school kids who had papers due or writing assignments. Apparently, there was a pretty lucrative market for this once you got known for being good at it and readily available.

Ekaterina was a tech whiz. She could fix computers and download programs and do the myriad things one could do with a computer if one only knew how. She worked under the table for a computer geek who had a store.

They both had obligations and meetings to go to in their home area. John and I both missed them when they left. I had thanked them for their help. They had helped me see sobriety could be fun and interesting as well as painful and aggravating.

I thanked John after they left for bringing them here. I told him I was touched by the thoughtfulness of the gesture and especially because it was so helpful to me. After saying that, we stood together looking at the ground, having a moment. After a moment, I broke the discomfort by pushing him and saying, "Don't be a bucket head."

He replied, "You're the bucket head," as he pushed me back.

15

Sobriety continued. I was working at it. Going to meetings day and night. I didn't warm up to a lot of people but there were a few really solid people I could talk to, Julie being the primary one. I remembered the suggestion and the benefit of staying close to a sponsor at least in early sobriety. I tried to talk to Julie most days. I would meet her at the meetings she went to and use John's cell phone to call her a couple of times a week. She encouraged my communication. It wasn't in my nature to talk and check in with anybody. She knew how hopelessly self-reliant and uncommunicative I could be and made it much easier by her gentle and affirming approach.

After my relapses I told her I would get serious with my efforts and started checking in more regular. Frankly somehow it helped. I wouldn't say much on the phone except that I was sober and which meeting I would be going to that day. She always asked me if I had run-ins with anyone. She knew I had a short fuse at times and wasn't afraid of mixing it up with someone. She knew I would fight if provoked.

Putting the drink down again brought up anger. I was grateful and hopeful and aware of Julie's help being a huge blessing, but I was angry. I radiated energy that said keep your distance. I didn't want anybody getting too close without being invited in. There were a few exceptions to that rule with people I had met and felt comfortable talking with.

There was also Tony. I had run into him at a meeting and had found out his meeting schedule and tried to meet with him once a week. Tony radiated anger and disliked most people, and I loved him for it. We both felt like outsiders in an outcast group. It's what made us friends. I also wanted to talk to him about John.

John had continued working for Tony and I wanted to know how he was doing. It turned out Tony was happy with John's work. He was picking up some knowledge and skill with the carpentry and that helped Tony a lot. But he was most impressed with his can-do attitude when it came to grunt work. Work like removing a pile of trash or ripping out the walls and old cabinets of a kitchen. He was depending and relying on John for that type of work more and more. Tony was skilled but like me didn't have the endurance he used to have. John never complained about any grunt work Tony had and the result was more projects and work for Tony and thus John.

I told Tony I was happy to hear John was working out well for him. I then told Tony about John asking me to be his guardian. Tony admitted that John had told him that. He looked me in the eye and simply said there would be no better guardian for John if I got sober. He then asked if I knew what I meant to John. I said yes and looked at the ground. Damn; I was having another moment.

16

Sue reached out to me through John. Or to be more precise, through John's cell phone. She wanted to get together. Which I knew primarily would be for what we referred to as stress relief. I talked with Julie about it. Julie questioned me about the relationship pretty thoroughly. When she learned it was mostly about sex without deeply held emotions, she was cautiously approving of it. There was one caveat.

If Sue was drinking heavy or at all, she was concerned I might relapse. She wanted me to ask Sue not to drink when she saw me. It seemed like a reasonable request. I called Sue and had a conversation with her. I told her sobriety had grown important to me again and I needed to know if she could abstain from drinking while we were together. She said as long as I continued to be good in bed, she didn't have a problem with it.

When I told Julie of this conversation she laughed and told me to have fun.

Julie's attitude frankly put me in mild shock. I grew up Irish Catholic. Sex was always wrong. From the thought to the act. Wrong and sinful.

To have someone whom I respected and was a bit of an authority figure to me as a sponsor have a common sense and open attitude about sex was something I hadn't anticipated.

Julie told me to read chapter five in the AA big book: to find the section about sex and read it. Which I did. It was the first common sense advice I had ever read about sex. It asked to ask yourself questions like "will having sex with this person cause jealousy?", which for me ruled out married women and women who had serious relationships going. I realized that my relationship with Sue didn't fail any of the parameters I had read. Terrific.

It was game on. Having gone and connected with my old girlfriend Celeste seemed to have reawakened my sexual desire. Sobriety and Sue had something to do with it also.

Sue and I got together. Both of us stone cold sober. At first it was strange. We were both a little self-conscious and awkward. We talked for a while and slowed down the process. Eventually we got to it. We both learned that it was not only possible to have sex sober, but it could also be more enjoyable.

17

Life and sobriety continued. I continued attending meetings religiously. I was still camping with John, and he was going off to work with Tony just about every day. We would still have some time together every day where we would talk. Often John would talk, and I would basically listen or ask a question for clarification about one of his stories. On occasion I would go off on a subject that I had a strong opinion about. I always told John to take mine and anyone else's opinion with a grain of salt and if it was an important subject to research it himself and form his own opinion.

I spent some time with Julie every week also. There were a few guys in AA I had gotten tentatively friendly with, but I couldn't wrap my mind around really talking with them. I was pretty open with Julie and felt comfortable talking and even asking her questions. When I realized I was asking her opinion about things and listening to her advice, I was amazed. I thought about it for a little while. I couldn't remember the last time I had asked anybody about anything for any reason. I sensed this was not a good way to live and started talking to Julie about it. Eventually she asked me a few questions about my childhood. We boiled it down to having been repeatedly embarrassed and shamed as a kid for not knowing things and asking questions.

After one instance I had made a decision. I made the pact that the price of knowing wasn't worth the cost. Worse still as I fleshed it out was I would pay any cost; I just wouldn't ever ask another question. *Fuck you.* I didn't care if I didn't know. Not a conscious decision but a powerful unconscious decision that profoundly affected the way I lived. Until now I never knew that had happened. Thinking about it even for a moment scared me to contemplate the cost of that decision.

Julie was a huge reason why I was sober. She had not only convinced me to go to a meeting, she had gotten through my extensive emotional armor I carried. She had really become a remarkable person. Not only was she a lawyer she was also a highly respected member of AA and was very active in doing service and helping others.

If I recalled correctly, I had about a dozen years on her. She had hit a nasty bottom with drugs, alcohol, and self-abuse at a young age. The upside was she had gotten sober, become a lawyer, and was still only about thirty years old.

Julie had appreciated my friendship immensely when she was struggling to get sober. She reminded me I had never judged her, never talked down to her, and had always encouraged her to keep coming. I had also always gone to great lengths to let her know she was powerless. Not weak or bad or defective but powerless. It was an important distinction. It had made a difference.

Unfortunately, I had relapsed and disappeared from the program. It was extremely gratifying to hear I had helped someone. Frankly, I recalled only part of what she had told me about.

I considered her friendship and help key to me being here in the program now. She gave me a sense of connection to the program and a place to vent. She also made me reflect on why I had relapsed. Talking with her was allowing me to become aware of some pitfalls that facilitated relapse in the past and could again in the future. One of the biggest was a lack of trust in a higher power. It was involved but becoming apparent it was hard to turn my life over to an entity I didn't really trust. I hadn't totally worked it out yet, but I was beginning to talk about it which often seemed like a huge first step for me.

18

John was acting strange. Strange for him anyway; he wasn't talking much. He was still working with Tony and sometimes coming back tired and sleepy. That was a possible reason that John wasn't talking a lot, telling me about his day and past life, but John was a talker and it hit me one night in the middle of an AA meeting that John had really backed off from talking to me. It dawned on me there was something up with John. The realization so startled me that I considered leaving the meeting to go check on him. After consideration I thought, *this is an ongoing thing and won't be a crisis in the next hour.*

At the end of the meeting, I talked with one person and then headed out. Concern about John was on my mind. If there was something up, I wanted to know about it. I needed cigarettes and found a store to buy them on the way back to camp. I smoked and walked slowly thinking about John and how I had a strong feeling there was something up with him. I had been with him long enough that I knew most of his life story by now. He seemed to tell me everything, so the troubling part was his lack of communication about something troubling him. I resolved to take my time but to draw him out if there was something there.

When I got back to camp, I expected to see him leaning against a tree reading a book as was often his habit. Instead, he was lying curled up in front of the fire weeping quietly. I sat down near him without saying anything and waited. After a time, he stopped crying and sat up and we both stared into the fire a while.

Finally, I said, "You going to tell me about it or am I going to have call you a bucket head or something?"

He started telling me about a friend from the past he had run into. She had changed dramatically since he had seen her two years previous. They had lived in a group home together and had taken the same bus to school. They had become fast friends and close confidants. She had left the group home abruptly when placed in a relative's care. They had lost touch after that.

Because they had been close and confidants in the past, he had managed to cajole out of her what was going on. She had been being sexually abused by a minister in her church and had told her guardian who didn't believe her, and the abuse continued. She had started to feel hopeless and was intimating she would harm or kill herself if things didn't change soon.

I told John I was really sorry to hear that. I then asked how long ago he had heard about this. He told me he had run into her a month ago and had found out about the abuse three weeks ago. He had been running into her in a park that he walked by after working for Tony. He had been hanging with her some after work.

I pondered this information for a bit. The question that was begging to be asked was why he had not told me about this earlier. At least to talk about it. He had told me his life story often with fairly intimate details. What was different about this?

"John, why is it that you hadn't told me about this before now?" I asked.

"Because I didn't want to get you involved, because it's a really fucked up situation and very dangerous for many reasons, and because

I really liked this girl and I wanted to ask for your help in the worst way, but I didn't want to mess up your life."

Whoa, I thought. This needs some clarification. After talking with John and drawing the facts out, it turned out his friend was named Lilly and she was an African American girl. They went to the same school and would ride the bus together. She was a year younger and one grade behind John. John and Lilly had become fast friends, confiding things about their lives and their troubles and fears. They had grown quite close. This was three years ago, when John was twelve and Lilly was eleven. Their friendship was a bright light in both their troubled lives.

Lilly was abruptly pulled out of the group home and placed with a relative against Lilly's own wishes. They had lost touch then because the relative lived in a different city. This city here being where her relatives lived. John had been crushed when she left. He had lost a friend, a confidant, and the one person he felt he could talk to in his short, turbulent life. He hadn't seen her again until a month ago.

He had been shocked by her seeming indifference to his presence. He had expected a certain amount of joyful surprise upon meeting again. Those were the feelings John had experienced, and he was surprised and hurt that she hadn't reciprocated them. John surmised that there was something really wrong in his friend Lilly's life.

Lilly hung out in an inner-city park at a certain time after school waiting for her guardians to get out of work and give her a ride to their home. There she would sit on a bench and read a book or do homework or listen to music. John had gone to the park after work every day in a quest to find out what was wrong with his friend Lilly.

The park was a known hangout of the local drug dealer who had eyes and ears all over the park. His control over the park made it a safe place for Lilly because she was known. No violence or shenanigans were allowed in the park because they would bring unwanted attention and affect the main business of the park. The main business being maintaining a safe place for the drug kingpin to hold court. A place that was controlled by him.

The dealer liked natural things to happen in the park like seeing young mothers with their babies and people sitting on benches doing normal things. It gave the impression of nothing going on here.

John had concluded this after being confronted by some young gang members who asked him point blank what he was doing there. He had told them the truth and they had confirmed that with Lilly. John also stuck out a bit for being white in a predominantly minority area. John had asked Lilly about what was going on and she had explained what she knew, which was fairly common knowledge amongst the local populace.

There was no drug dealing in this park. This was where the kingpin would hold court and meet with people. No doubt it was one of the safest areas in the inner city because of that.

Which was one of the reasons John didn't want to tell me about it. He figured I would get involved and have a run in with one of the young hoods watching the park. Lilly wasn't allowed to stray from the park once she got there. This made the park the one option in John's mind.

"What makes you so sure that I would do something?" I asked him. "Clearly this is none of my business."

After a long moment John said, "Because I would have asked you despite not wanting to."

John abruptly lied down and after a moment began weeping silently again.

19

The following day I asked John to confirm some things from his friend Lilly. Things like the name of the minister who was abusing her and how or when the minister was getting access to her.

I also asked him to get the name of the drug dealer if he could. John looked at me quizzically and said, "You're not going to be able to do anything."

"I'm not planning on doing anything. Just get the information," I told him.

I had to clear my head, so I went to a 10 a.m. meeting

I knew of one that wasn't too much of a hike. I didn't get any answers at the meeting but it did quiet my thoughts a little so I could think.

I thought about talking with Julie and getting advice from her about the situation John was in. I hesitated and decided against it. Julie was wonderful but would get very upset at any hint of violence and this situation felt fraught with potential violence to me. I had described a few minor fights I had been in in the past and had noticed Julie's change of demeanor and discomfit. She didn't like even hearing about violent incidents from the past, never mind current situations that could become violent.

I knew I had to find someone else to talk to. In reality I didn't have a lot of options. Even the idea of talking to someone about a problem or situation was only because of my sobriety and newfound habit of talking things out encouraged by Julie. I had one other person to talk to: Tony. Tony had been there and done that. Violence was a large part of his story. He knew the ramifications and risks of this world and was the one I would talk to.

I took a leisurely walk in the afternoon and walked a large circle around the park that John had described to me. I worked hard at being covert, but the park was carefully watched, and I knew I was seen and observed by several young men.

I went to Tony's house around 6 p.m. hoping he would be done with work and John wouldn't still be here. I timed it well on both counts and Tony was in his kitchen making himself a meal. He asked if I'd like a burger and some salad. I almost said no when I realized I would actually love both of those things. I agreed and he got an extra plate out of his cupboard and told me to grab a seat.

I watched him as he finished cooking the burgers and brought them over to the kitchen table. He had some nice-looking rolls and condiments on the table already. We both helped ourselves to some salad and dressed up our burgers to our own liking. We engaged in a little small talk, and I asked him how John was working out. He said he had no complaints, which coming from Tony was high praise. He said he was able to get a nice lucrative job because John had helped finish up two others in a timely fashion.

"I vaguely remember having his energy in the past," Tony stated with a rueful smile.

We engaged in some program and other small talk while we ate. After dinner I was grateful that he made us both a cup of coffee. I lit up a cigarette and started telling him about John's friend Lilly and how it affected John. I told him I didn't know what to do or say to John other than telling him it was too bad.

Tony told me John had told him about the situation and John was quite obviously very bothered by his friend's condition. Then he surprised me by asking me when I was going to make a move on the minister. Startled I asked him what made him so sure I would do anything about this situation or make a move on the minister whom I knew nothing about.

"You can't stop being you."

That reply pissed me off to no end. It implied that I didn't have a choice or something. I told him as much and we talked for a while about the situation. Eventually he said he wasn't trying to piss me off with that comment but rather considered it a compliment. He thought of me as the guy who could and probably would right that wrong. Not totally appeased but definitely appreciative of having someone to talk about the situation with, I left an hour later. I caught the better part of a meeting before I headed back to camp to check on John.

I was somewhat relieved to find John fast asleep when I got there. I felt like I needed some time to think about things before I talked with John again. I had just finally gotten sober, and this was a potentially very volatile situation if I got involved. I wanted to ask John a few questions for clarification.

"Shit," I said out loud to no one in particular. I was going to get involved. I could feel it. Tony was right. I couldn't let it slide, and my intuition just told me I'd be involved despite whatever new information I gleaned. *Damn*, I thought. I had just got gotten sober and was working toward a simple, quiet life!

I thought about the abuse that John's friend was enduring. Nothing I could think of could mitigate the severity of what was going on or the intensity of the harm that it would cause. I felt the rage rise and thought, *fuck it. Let the cards fall where they may, this is going to stop.*

20

The next morning John and I went to breakfast. He was very quiet. Not his normal condition. He liked to talk and as a rule would be talking about his work with Tony, his past life or whatever came to mind.

We ate our food quietly and after I ordered a second coffee. I asked if he had gotten the information I wanted. He said yes and gave me the name of the minister and where he lived. He also knew of the hall he preached out of every Sunday.

I asked John how the minister was getting access to his friend Lilly. He said the aunt and uncle caring for her would let her sleep over the minister's place in the guise of doing office work and house-work for the minister. That was when the abuse would occur. She was afraid to mention it again because it caused so much turmoil and violent emotional reactions in the house when she had mentioned it previously.

Lilly felt trapped with no exit. The proverbial rock and a hard place. Suffer the abuse or create a horror show in the home. I could see that was why Lilly was suicidal. Suicide could look attractive when there was no way out.

I could go round and round with thoughts on this situation, but

I kept ending up at the same place. The abuse needed to stop, and soon. If relatives and society had failed this girl, then I would make that happen.

Period, decision made.

Sobriety could suck sometimes but I loved the way I could get clear on something and make a decision without wavering and wobbling all over the place. I would do something to stop this abuse.

I asked John if Lilly knew about me and how we first met.

He said, "Yes."

"I need to talk to her in person and ask her about the abuse briefly but when I confirm everything, I will stop it," I told him.

John looked out the window and just started weeping. Frankly this surprised me. I expected him to be happy but not to start weeping. I thought, *is he in love with this girl or something?*

"John, how is it that I saved you from a horrendous ordeal and you said thanks, but in this situation where I might help your friend you start crying?"

After a moment with tears in his eyes John looked at me. "Number one is you're not a 'might help' type of guy, and this abuse ain't right and you're willing to step up and maybe that's why."

With that he threw money on the table for the bill and said he had to go to work. Bewildered I watched him leave. I got myself a coffee to go and went across the street to a small park and lit up a cigarette.

I was on my second cigarette when it hit me. John was a survivor. He knew firsthand what Lilly was dealing with. I thought about that and the more I did the more it made sense. A couple of times when John was telling me about some abusive situations, he had gotten vague on me with the descriptions. Most of the time he was really clear on what had gone down. That and his reaction to me helping his friend had me now thinking that John had been sexually abused. I'd wait for the right moment, but I was going to ask him if that was true.

21

The following day John told me that Lilly was willing to meet me and talk about what was going on if there was a chance I would stop the abuse.

"There is that other big problem though," John declared.

"What's that?"

"You can't go and casually hang out there without tacit permission from the local drug dealer who hangs there."

With all the surprising revelations and emotional turmoil John had been through I had forgotten about that.

"Did you find out the name of the drug dealer?"

"Yes, it's a guy by the name of Adrian McKnight."

I knew him. His nickname was Organized Adrian because he was considered to have organized a drug gang that the Feds and locals hadn't been able to take down.

"He is smart, tough and ruthless," I replied

Smart, tough, and ruthless. *He was also pragmatic,* I thought. I told John so and said I would go speak to him today and I wanted John to set up a time when I'd talk to Lilly. John looked incredulous.

"You know him," he declared in a shocked tone of voice.

"Yeah," I mused, "I know him." It had been years since I had seen

Adrian. I had just hit the streets after losing yet another good job, a live-in girlfriend, and my apartment. That had led to turmoil, anger, rage, and more booze, lots more booze. I was half out of my mind with emotional pain, guilt, shame, and used booze, and fighting to alleviate and distract myself. I loved to fight. Living on and dealing with the streets, it was easy to find something to fight over. Eventually I would calm down but when I first hit the streets I fought constantly. I was angry and raging at my fate with no ability to own or look at my part in being there.

Which is how I had met Adrian. Back then there were two drug gangs vying for turf and power: Adrian's and another run by a guy named Ross. Ross had a couple of ruthless bodyguards that had always kept him safe. All of this unbeknownst to me at the time. The bodyguards had rolled up on me one evening when I was sitting on a bench nursing a good bottle of whiskey.

They had said they needed my bench and that I should move along. At that time, I prayed for shit like this just so I could get into a jam and start throwing hands. I had told them to go fuck themselves and maybe each other if they were into that. Clearly they hadn't expected nor did they like my answer.

One of them was a bit heavyset and one of them was thin and wiry. The thin one jumped first, pulling out a gun from his waist that had been hidden by a sweatshirt. I leapt up from the bench and grabbed his arm holding the gun with my left hand while swinging my right arm to connect with his face. I managed to get some leverage in my swing, and I could feel his nose break when my fist connected with it. The gun went off, shooting wildly in the air.

I followed up the first punch with a punch to the solar plexus which enabled me to wrestle the gun out of his hand. The gun dropped on the ground, and I instinctively grabbed him and put him between me and the heavyset guy. The heavyset guy had gotten his gun out and shot just when I swung the wiry guy between us. The bullet hit the wiry guy and the shock of shooting his friend gave me the time I needed to move on him.

I kicked the gun in his outstretched hand and hit him fast with two viciously hard punches. It hurt him enough so I could go after his gun and wrestle it away. After which I pummeled him with punches until he was unconscious. I was enraged that this had turned into a win or die death match for myself.

The wiry guy was shot in the stomach and looked rough. The heavyset guy was out cold and there were people heading towards us to see what was going on which I took as my cue to leave. I didn't want to have to explain to the police or anyone else for that matter what had happened or why.

After this incident I didn't leave the area but stayed well clear of the park where the fight had gone down. I was living in some woods about a mile from the park, and there were many other areas in this city to hang out and drink in.

A week after the incident I was eating a late lunch in a diner I favored. A Cadillac SUV rolled to a stop in front of the diner. Four African American men got out and walked over to a young kid who was sitting on the curb whom I had noticed previously. They chatted a bit and the kid took off. Three of the men took positions in front of the diner. The fourth walked into the diner, walked over to my booth, and slid casually into the seat opposite me. We regarded each other for several moments.

He had a shaved head and cold dark eyes. I knew this had to have something to do with my interactions with the two fellows in the park the other night. I was definitely wary and concerned with this situation but somehow I didn't feel in danger. After saying nothing for several moments, I decided to finish my burger and continued eating. After I finished, we regarded each other for a couple more moments.

Finally, he said, "You're not an easy guy to find."

I nodded and said, "The kid out front who you talked to spotted me?"

He nodded and said, "I had to meet the guy who took out Ross's top two guys."

After another long moment in which I didn't respond, he asked, "Would you like to come work with me?"

Surprised, I considered the question. "In what capacity would you have me work?" I answered.

"Security with an eye towards management."

I thought for a moment. He was definitely into drugs and everything that came with dealing drugs. I definitely would have no part of that as I considered money from drugs blood money. I told him his world wasn't for me.

"Yet you take down two of the baddest enforcers in the game," he countered.

This comment got my attention. Had I taken out his guys or what? He saw my apprehension and smiled slightly telling me not to worry. "They weren't my guys," he said.

It turned out they were the muscle of a rival gang he had been fighting with over turf. He intimated I had tipped the scales greatly in his favor by taking those two out. The head of the gang was vulnerable without his ace bodyguards around.

I asked him what had happened to the two guys. I considered the question a mistake because with that question I confirmed my involvement.

"One was dead and the other one had disappeared."

He asked for an honest answer of why I wouldn't consider working for him. I answered him honestly that he was in an evil business that I just couldn't be part of. He asked if I judged him for his involvement.

"No but I would judge myself unmercifully to the point I would have no effectiveness. If I lived your life who knows where I'd be or what I'd do," I added.

He regarded my answer and seemed satisfied with my replies.

"Well, if you're in the park again, don't be taking out any more guys because they're probably with me. I'll leave word to let the crazy white guy drink on his bench though," he said with a wry smile. The last comment seemed to be letting me know he knew how it started as well.

As he was leaving, I asked, "Do I have to worry about Ross coming back on me?"

He turned, looked me in the eye, and said, "No, Ross won't be a problem."

With that he walked out, got back into his SUV with his cohorts, and left. That was my one and only encounter with Adrian McKnight. I was in and out of this city several times since then and his power and influence had grown substantially. He was known as the top dog in the drug dealing world and controlled the drug trade in the whole city. One would hear stories and cautionary tales about crossing him. Now I was going to ask him for permission to hang on his turf a bit. I thought about not bothering but he was pretty thorough with knowing things back years ago. No doubt nothing gets by his attention. It didn't feel like an option. I would go talk to him and tell him what I was up to.

22

I asked John if he knew what time Adrian would be in the park.

"He's usually there from 2 p.m. on."

I nodded and considered taking John with me but after a moment decided to go alone. I told him that if he saw Lilly to set up a meet with her for tomorrow sometime if possible. John went off to work with Tony and I headed out to find a morning meeting. The meeting turned out to be a step meeting and they were on the third step. "Make a decision to turn our will and our lives over to the care of God as we understood God."

I wondered what God would think of my plan. I had real trust issues and problems with God, but I was trying to work them out with Julie. I thought about the fact that I was thinking about someone else's problem and not thinking of my own. Maybe, just maybe that was a start. I said a prayer for a good outcome. Not my usual MO when dealing with problems but I noticed I felt calmer when I left the meeting. I made a mental note to try and remember this.

I took a slow leisurely walk for an hour heading in the general direction of the park to see if I could meet Adrian. I found a place I knew to have a quick lunch before the big meet. If it turned south, I figured it would be better to get in a jam with something in my stomach.

I realized I was nervous and started judging myself for being so. I brought myself up sharply when I reminded myself that I was planning to meet with the area's biggest drug dealer and if I wasn't nervous that would be a sign of something being wrong with me. I finished my lunch and headed to the park.

Twenty minutes later I walked into the park from an area which gave me plenty of sight lines in all directions. There was a series of benches several hundred yards away that had a group of men hanging around. I figured this was where he would probably be, and I started slowly walking in that direction. When I was within twenty yards, four men started to converge on me from three different directions.

Shit, I thought, *this guy really was organized.*

Within ten more yards, I had three guys in front of me blocking my path. They were joined by a fourth and none of them looked like lightweights. They were all in their late teens, early twenties in age. They were all also hardcore with two in particular that looked like stone-cold killers. One of those two asked me where I was going.

I answered, saying, "I'd like to talk to Adrian."

He countered with, "What's your business?"

I thought about that quickly and decided not to tell him. I said, "That's between me and Adrian."

He looked like he'd rather shoot me than deal with me anymore but ended up asking what my name was. I told him I was the whiskey drinking crazy white guy.

"You'll be the dead white guy in a moment if Adrian don't know you."

He sent one of the others off in the direction of the aforementioned benches and stayed right in front of me with the other three thugs. The fourth guy came back and nodded at my new best friend. He looked at me and said, "It's your lucky day."

The others moved so I could walk toward the middle of the park again. I started walking, thinking that I had met some tough guys and some really scary guys, but he was a combination of tough and scary I would never want to deal with. When I got close to the benches two other guys closed in on me. One of them said, "We're going to pat you down." I nodded and let them. They were thorough. After which one of them pointed in the direction I should walk and after a few more steps I saw Adrian sitting on a bench nearby. I walked over to him. and we regarded each other for a long moment.

I had just worked it out. It had been nine years since I had last seen him. He had aged a little and looked thinner. Stress no doubt. I broke the quiet impasse with the comment, "It's been a while." He nodded and asked how life was treating me. I told him I was trying to get used to not drinking.

Adrian chuckled softly with, "Yeah, I recall you being contentious under the influence."

"Contentious." How many drug dealers had vocabularies like that? *Who knows*, I thought, *maybe all the top ones have good vocabularies and that's why they are top dealers*. Adrian was in a hard game, and you could still find him in the same park, at the same time, at the same place nine years later. Impressive in its own right.

After another quiet moment of regarding each other he asked me what I wanted. I told him my young friend John had a friend, Lilly, who hung out in this park in the afternoon whom I would like to come and talk to. John found out that she was being abused by a local minister and I decided to investigate.

"What will you do if you find out he is abusing her?" Adrian asked.

"I will stop it."

Adrian nodded at that reply. "Is this sort of thing a specialty of yours?" he asked.

"No. I am involved in this only because of young John."

"And John is?" he asked.

"A surrogate son of sorts." It was the quickest most effective way to answer the question. He considered my answers and nodded slightly.

After several more moments of quiet and regarding each other he stated, "Anyone else gave me those answers, I wouldn't believe them. But I believe you're telling me the truth." He closed with, "Interview the girl here but stay clear of this park after that." With that I was dismissed, and I left.

It had been a surreal experience, and, without any seeming organization, things were very well organized. Adrian was impressive. It was hard to believe he wouldn't be a success in many other businesses. Thoughtful, intuitive, and smart. One could forget his business at least until they had to deal with his cohorts. I thought about the one that had confronted me first. He was scary. Perhaps a prerequisite for a drug dealer. A scary, stone cold killer enforcer!

23

I made my way back to camp and met up with John. We took a walk to a local restaurant that had good food and was reasonably priced. John asked me if I had met Adrian and I told him I had and I was cleared to meet his friend Lilly in the park.

I asked, "Can you set it for tomorrow?"

He said he thought he could.

"How did you know Adrian and why would he let me of all people meet in the park?"

I thought about telling him but decided now wasn't the time.

"After this business with your friend is finished, I will tell you."

John made a face but didn't argue which was a sign the business with his friend was of vital importance to him. I had originally encouraged him to challenge people in their statements, including me. I had begun to regret that with his constant arguments, feeling like I had opened up a Pandora's box. On the other hand, I was happy to see him speaking up because I think doing so boosted his self-confidence.

24

I met John the next day on the outskirts of the park. We walked into the park and sat on a bench near the edge and waited for Lilly. Within minutes Lilly came walking down the street. John jumped up to go and meet her. They talked for a moment and John gestured to me and they walked over.

John introduced us and we both said hello. She was a pretty young girl. Her hair was twisted into braids and wrapped with elastics. A look I was more used to seeing on younger girls. Her affect seemed flat, and her eyes had a lack of light and spirit.

I asked John if he could take a walk so we could be alone for a few minutes. John complied and I explained to Lilly that John had told me what was happening and that she wanted it to stop. She nodded her head. I told her it was my understanding that the abuse was sexual in nature. She nodded her head yes again. I felt like I was at an impasse. The manner in which I was contemplating stopping the abuse was not only illegal, it was violent and definitely risky. I needed more than a head nod.

On the other hand, I had to ask a fourteen-year-old girl details about sex which was more than a little bit uncomfortable. I had a new respect for the professionals who dealt with this. I took a deep breath. I explained to Lilly that before I did anything I needed confirmation from her what was going on. I apologized to her but asked her for details of exactly what was happening. To my surprise and slight embarrassment, she explained in detail what was going on, looking at me the whole time. She told me the minister was having oral sex with her and it felt horrible and then he made her give him oral sex. She looked down at the end, slightly embarrassed and looking sad.

I told her it was really a terrible thing that this was happening to her, and I was really sorry, and it made me really sad too. She looked at me with incredulity for a moment. I remembered John had told me she had told someone but hadn't been believed. I wondered if the incredulity was because of that. She had been very believable in the telling. Frankly I would be shocked if this wasn't true. I made my decision.

I asked her when she was going to see the minister again. She said she wasn't sure but probably next week. I asked her how long the abuse had been going on. She told me two years.

Two years!!? Two years with no-one coming to her aid! We sat there quietly for a few minutes. Me with the attempt of wrapping my mind around the implications of sexual abuse that started at the age of twelve. My attempt failed and I got focused back on Lilly. I told Lilly she had a good friend in John who became very upset when he heard about how she was being abused. I told her the reason I was going to stop the abuse was because John had asked.

When the truth of what I was telling her hit her she asked, "Really?"

I nodded and said, "Really, and John is a really good friend." I emphasized, "Really."

She gave me a slight smile when I said that. Several minutes later, John came back and when he got close, she jumped up and ran over and gave him a hug. John was taken aback by this. Despite squirming a little she held on to him and after a moment he surrendered to the hug which was full of hope and trust and friendship.

25

I shadowed the minister for three days. I got a sense of his habits and routine. I also discovered he had another young woman staying overnight at times who definitely looked underage. I decided I wanted to make my play in his apartment. Which meant I needed to catch him alone. He lived in a three-story apartment building with a door buzzer. The buzzer would be easy to beat. Ideally, I'd like to get in his apartment and get the lay of the land some beforehand. I needed some tools. I had to see Tony. If he didn't have them, he'd know where I could get them.

I found Tony coming back from a job in his van with John riding shotgun. They both acted happy to see me. It gave me a strange feeling I didn't have time to work out. John was exuberant, talking about the new job they had scored in a real high-end house, a house which was hundreds of years old. Tony was taking the time to explain the differences in lumber over time periods. Lumber from one period meant a better wood or an old forest growth wood which was different from lumber from a different period. I could see how that might be interesting, but it didn't seem to warrant John's ebullience. Tony looked to be in a good mood too. He looked happy. It looked strange on him. It was the best way to describe it. I had seen Tony laugh, but

I don't ever recall seeing him with this look. He just looked happy. I had a poignant moment. I ran through memories again. No. I had never seen Tony look happy. Which begged the question in my mind, *had Tony ever been happy?*

I ran down a quick timeline of what I knew about his life: A childhood full of neglect and abuse, then violent and addiction fueled adolescence, followed by reform schools, stints in prison, and more addiction. Then he got sober, had relapses, had health problems, and always was on the edge with money. He was eleven months clean now, fifty-two years old, and for the first time in my knowledge looked happy. *Could happiness find its way to one for the first time at fifty-two?* I stayed on that thought for a moment until I got blindsided by the question, *had I ever really been happy?*

Gratefully Tony had finished parking his van and taking equipment and trash out of it. He invited me inside for a coffee. John put some things away and said goodbye because he had a couple of errands to run.

I started my conversation with Tony by asking him why John was so happy. Tony told me he had just spent the last half-hour praising John's work and given him a big raise. I asked him if he really talked for half an hour before giving it.

He said, "Yeah, I didn't mind the raise but trying to explain why almost killed me." We both had a good laugh. Tony's sparse use of words was a running joke between us. The solid truth of his statement made it all the more humorous.

Having discovered the why for John's good mood I ventured to ask Tony why he seemed happy. He gave me one of his smile's which distorted his face so much because it was so rare.

"I've met someone."

Well, I'll be a monkey's uncle; Tony was in love. I felt joy for him. I couldn't think of a more deserving guy to find someone to be happy with. Especially with the hard life I knew that he had. I told him I was really happy for him and glad he had found someone. He asked me to come around in about a month to meet her when he was having a small gathering. He told me he was going to propose this weekend and the gathering would be of close friends to celebrate. He told me her name was Beth and gave me some details about how they had met. Beth was in AA too and had a solid sobriety of ten years clean. He went on about her and her accomplishments for another five minutes. *Good Lord*, I thought, *he really was in love.*

After a while I finally got down to business and asked Tony if he had any lock picking tools. He looked at me askance with the question, "What for?" hanging in the air. I told him he had been right. I wasn't going to let the situation with Lilly slide without doing something about it and I needed the tools to pick the lock of the minister's apartment.

He nodded and had me follow him out to his garage where he had a dozen toolboxes of varying shapes and sizes. He started sifting through an old looking one 'til he found a set of lock picking tools. He showed them to me and had me follow him to the back of the garage where he had a couple old doors with locks on them so he could give me instruction. He showed me how to use them and then had me practice several times until he was satisfied.

After I left, I recalled him telling me one of his stays in prison was over being caught red handed in a burglary.

Like I had said before, he was handy.

26

I picked the lock of the minister's apartment when I knew he wasn't home and let myself in. The following night, Lilly was supposed to be there. I didn't want her coming back here again. I wanted Lilly to be done with the minister. My task this night was to make that happen. I wasn't sure how I was going to do that, but I had a few vague ideas.

I walked around and got the layout of the apartment. After that I settled in a chair near the door. An hour later the minister came home. I opted for a simple first approach and put the minister in a choke hold that would make one pass out after a few minutes. I worried about his resistance to this but found him surprisingly weak and ineffectual. He was in poor physical shape. When he passed out, I placed him on the floor and zipped tied his ankles and wrists. I took one of his ties and place it in his mouth and tied it tightly around his head.

Several minutes later he started coming around. It took him several more minutes to realize his circumstances and where he was. Then the fear settled in. Time to go to work. He started moving around a lot to try to improve his circumstances.

Despite being zip tied hand and foot, I didn't want him moving and announced he was not to move or suffer the consequences. He started moaning and trying to talk despite the gag in his mouth. I then told him to stay quiet. He complied. I was out of visual sight of him and just announced my orders. I figured I'd give him some real time to bring up some terror. Ten minutes later when he started moving again, I went over and punched him in the face three times and calmly told him the instructions were to not move. I then walked out of eyesight again. Thirty minutes later I figured the terror had settled in well enough to deal with him.

I told him why I was there. I was there to stop him from abusing underage girls, especially Lilly. I explained his death would be the best approach. I asked him what he thought of that. I then took the gag off.

It turned out he had a torrent of things to say. He started with denial but ended that when I threatened him with torture if he continued to lie. I also told him I had a camera hidden in the apartment and I had video proof. The latter was a lie, but it induced a reluctant admission of some possible inappropriate behavior.

I got him talking about the abuse which was something I wanted because I had a small pocket tape recorder going. I wanted a confession on tape that I could threaten him with also.

Somewhere in his babbling he started intimating that Lilly was responsible for his behavior. This was where I lost it for a bit and pulled out a gun.

It was a snub nosed thirty-eight caliber I had obtained from the streets. I put two bullets in it and spun the chamber in front of him. I point blank asked him if he was going to stop abusing girls. Then I pulled the trigger. Click: empty chamber. I had him focused now. I opened the revolver showed him the two bullets again and then closed it and spun the chamber. Click: empty chamber again. I repeated the same process quickly and did it again. Click: empty chamber again.

I took a breath and got control of myself. I realized a part of me wanted to kill him. I took several more deep breaths and brought myself back to my task. The minister must have realized his peril as he seemed to have soiled himself and was shaking and begging for his life.

He was ready. I told him he needed to move out of the area immediately and never come back. I told him he was to never see Lilly or the other young girl he was abusing again. I told him to be gone in twenty-four hours.

Then I asked him if he had any questions. He didn't. I then asked him if I needed to tell him what would happen if he didn't comply with my demands. He said no.

I spent a little while showing the minister some other things that could happen if he didn't comply. Pain I'd be willing to inflict on his body. I left with the announcement the clock was ticking on his moving date. He had twenty-four hours.

Afterwards I took a long walk. A long circuitous route back to camp. During the walk I found a bridge over a river where I dropped my handgun. After walking for an hour, I started to calm down a bit. I had scared myself with my game of Russian roulette. Three times lucky. I wondered the odds on that. It scared me because I hadn't planned nor did I want to murder the minister. I had wanted to scare him, which I did. I hadn't expected the emotion I got caught up with which almost cost the minister his life and a possible murder charge for myself.

The good thing about my actions was I was fairly certain the minister wouldn't be here in twenty-four hours.

27

The following day I woke up late, having had a really hard time falling asleep. I was satisfied with the way I had dealt with the minister. He didn't have the gall to not comply. I was still high on adrenaline and anxiety. It scared me how close I had come to killing him. I tried hard to let those thoughts go, but they kept coming back.

I found a noon time meeting to attend. I didn't really listen too much with my racing mind, but it calmed me a little. I decided I was in need of two things. I needed to spend a night with Sue, and I needed to talk with Tony. It would take at least a day or two to get together with Tony, so I borrowed a phone from a friend and called Sue. I asked her if she was free that evening. She was. I felt intense relief and realized these intense feelings were the reason I drank and would relapse. I knew a night with Sue would help distract me and help me stay sane.

Hopefully I could get together with Tony the following night and talk some of this through. I would reach out to Tony through John and see him as soon as possible. I considered talking some of this out with my sponsor Julie but decided against it because of the illegality and violence involved.

Sue had me come over after she got home from work, and we ate some Thai takeout she had bought. She told me about the current status of her job as a child welfare case worker and the improvements they were trying to make. She still had too big a caseload and that didn't seem like it would change anytime soon. However, a new department head was making things more organized and advocated well for her workers. It had given Sue hope. For a moment I considered talking with Sue about the minister before violently rejecting the idea in my mind. After a bit we got down to what we both needed: some good sex. I think I was amorous a little longer than usual. The following morning, she woke me as she was about to leave, saying there was coffee left in the pot and to help myself. She asked me to make sure I locked up when I left. Walking out the door, she said whatever I had been doing recently I should continue with because she loved the intensity it gave me. I smiled thinking to myself, *if she only knew.*

It was three more nights before I could get together with Tony. I made plans through John who was working with him every day. I had been hitting meetings and had calmed down some from the violent intensity of my meeting with the minister. I still felt like talking it out in a safe place would be very helpful. I needed to keep my perspective and my emotions as level as possible.

Talking with Tony was my answer for that.

Tony was super busy but wanted to accommodate me. He asked me to meet him at a local pub which served good food but also had live music on weekends. He said there was a live jazz band with a real good singer that he wanted to hear. We talked about the fact there was alcohol served, and we both decided we were okay with that and if either of us was uncomfortable with it we could leave.

I arrived at the pub looking forward to both the music and talking with Tony. When I walked in, the sad soulful sound of Sade was playing softly as background music. It set a nice mood. The place seemed well worn but cozy and familiar somehow. Ideal for jazz or folk type music. I found a booth where I could see the band while they played.

They were setup across the room. I ordered a coffee and an appetizer and told the waiter I would be joined by a friend soon.

After a few minutes, I got bored and found a house paper at the bar. I was immersed in an article when the band came out and started warming up. There was a bass and piano player. Five minutes later they started their first song. An African American woman had joined the musicians as the vocalist. The voice on her was stunning. I put the paper down to watch her sing. I hadn't caught the title, but I thought they had credited Nina Simone for making the song a hit. The arrangement was slow which fit her voice and delivery.

The woman had high cheekbones, coffee colored skin, and was very attractive. She also had thin braids on her head which were gathered with something at the back of her head. Then she had wrapped her head with some sort of colorful garment. She also had on a colorful blouse and different colored skirt with a colorful scarf to round off the shock of colors. The colors of the different garments looked artfully chosen if a little busy. The effect was that she looked like she had been dressed by Monet and Matisse.

She announced an Ella Fitzgerald tune and continued in a wonderfully slow and soulful arrangement. The bassist and the piano player were in sync with her. They watched her intently for their cues. They were also very good. This trio seemed to have played together often. I knew Tony was into jazz and blues music, but I hadn't expected such a good singer and band to be there.

The stunning performance continued. I started wondering if I had this wrong and looked around the room. The pub had filled up. People were paying attention and engrossed in the performance just as I was. This group had a following! People seemed to be enthralled with the singer and band. I was mildly shocked they were playing there and not in some sort of much fancier venue with a much larger audience. She, at the very least, was that good.

The singer had all slow arrangements. Or possibly she was slowing the arrangement down to fit her mood. She struck me as being a bit sad like she had suffered a loss. It started showing up in her delivery when she would hang a phrase in the air for an extra beat or two. She would then pick up the tune with a sad soulful timbre in her voice that I had never experienced before. The effect was extraordinary. It made a soulful song and singer more soulful. She reached the inner psyche. I felt moved in places in my body that I didn't know I had. It was a soulful, mournful, and moving interpretation of jazz songs. I wasn't a huge jazz enthusiast, but I always picked up on good vocalists when I heard them no matter the music genre.

During one particularly mournful tune, I glanced around the room again. There was a couple sitting not far from me at a table in the middle of the room. The woman was elegant and had a martini glass sitting on the table in front of her. Several tears were streaming from her left eye as she watched the singer. It seemed appropriate that the singer would have that effect. It also confirmed for me that I wasn't alone in being moved by this performance.

She announced a final song of the set before a break. I knew the song, but I couldn't place it. It wasn't a jazz tune but a pop tune from somewhere. She was halfway through before I figured it out. It was "Superstar" made famous by Karen Carpenter. She had slowed the song down by half with her interpretation and made it her own.

I always liked that song and would have said nobody could do better than Karen Carpenter's interpretation yet here it was. Her delivery of one of the lines in the refrain was the perfect ending of the most remarkable set of tunes I had ever heard. "Baby, baby, baby, baby ohh baby" sung in a slow, sad soulful way. The room broke into enthusiastic applause as she closed the set. I felt like I had witnessed something that was rare to experience in one's lifetime. I was processing this when Tony walked in and slid into the opposite side of the booth.

"What did I miss?" he asked.

"Just the most remarkable set of music I have ever heard."

He gave me one of his smiles that looked so awkward on him. His attempts at smiling made him look strange at best.

"Damn," he continued, "I hate that I'm late."

He then told me he had seen her once before and had a similar experience. Tony then confirmed a lot of what I had heard and felt during the performance. The soulful delivery and its effect. I felt grateful I had someone to talk to about it who could validate what I had experienced.

While the band was on break, I gave Tony a thumbnail version of my time with the minister. I admitted to him how I had scared myself with how close I had come to ending his life. I confessed that a part of me was hoping the gun would go off despite the probable dire consequences.

Tony looked amused and said, "Well you did focus his attention."

I then described the other creative ways I had used to convince the minister to stop abusing young girls and in particular Lilly. Tony was great. He took in everything I had told him and said he didn't think any of it would come back on me.

"The minister's got too much to lose by complaining to anyone," he continued.

Tony would be honest on this type of feedback. If he thought there would be trouble, he would tell me and help me make a plan to deal with it. Tony knew his way around the dark side.

I felt a rush of relief. Talking to Tony was a tremendous help. I had been hanging on to all this emotional turmoil over my actions for three days and now felt unburdened. I then described to Tony that I felt he was the only one I could trust with the telling of this type of incident. I also told him how much I appreciated that and him. We had an awkward moment that was interrupted by the band members picking at their instruments in preparation for the second set.

Five minutes later the singer came back. She started adjusting her music stand and mic. While I was watching her, she looked directly at me. I held her gaze. Eventually she got off the small stage they were on and started walking towards me looking at me most of the way. My mind raced. Did I know her from somewhere? Did I meet her in a blackout? Did I hit on her drunk sometime? My thoughts did not run in a positive vein.

She got to the table and said, "Hi." She glanced and nodded at Tony then looked back at me.

We regarded each other until she finally said, "I hear you're a friend to the oppressed."

Holding back panic, I calmly stated, "I have no idea what you're talking about."

After another moment passed, she said, "Of course not." She then immediately asked if I had a request or favorite jazz tune. My mind still in a tizzy about her first comment I couldn't think of a thing. After a moment she gave me a gentle prod, saying, "Well."

Finally feeling desperate I said, "How about, 'Imagine' by John Lennon."

She smiled and said, "You got it," then turned and gracefully sauntered back to the small podium to continue her preparation for the second set.

Tony looked at me with a quizzical look. I looked back at him and simply shrugged my shoulders. I discovered I had been holding my breath and let out a long sigh and took several real deep breaths.

"Apparently she knows about the other night."

"How?"

"I have no idea but what else could she be referencing?" I thought about it some more and simply stated, "I don't know how but she knows."

As soon as I finished that statement, she started her second set with the song "Young and foolish." I had heard Tony Bennett sing that song before. Again, she made it her own, leaving some of the audience in tears with their own memories of being young and foolish.

After several more tunes, the singer announced a request for someone who was a friend to the oppressed. She then sang my request of
"Imagine" by John Lennon.

I had felt foolish that I hadn't come up with a jazz tune as a request.
It turned out I was glad I hadn't. Her slow soulful rendition was her
crowning achievement of the evening as far as I was concerned. The
patrons applauded resoundingly after her performance. Until hearing
it I couldn't have thought that this tune would lend itself to a soulful
interpretation. If you weren't listening to the words, her rendition
would have had you think it was another song. After, she announced
and took another break.

I looked at Tony. He slowly shook his head and said, "Unbelievable." After a moment he continued with, "She's the best jazz vocalist
I've ever heard."

I was in turmoil. Partly from having witnessed such an exceptional
performance but mostly from her comments about being a friend to
the oppressed. The only thing I could think of was that she had some
sort of connection to Lilly. Was she a neighbor, an aunt, a cousin?
My mind was all over the place with possibilities. I vented more with
Tony about this during the break. He pointed out that if she did know
she certainly didn't take any umbrage to what I had done but rather
was calling me a friend to the oppressed. In which case maybe I ought
to relax about it all and let it go.

Tony was a life saver. This was the type of thing I could obsess
on for forever and a day. I also noted another occasion when I talked
about something instead of obsessing about it by myself. I got a lot
of relief. I wasn't ready to let go of it completely but it helped a lot to
talk with Tony. Which was good because it enabled me to hear and
enjoy the third and final set of the evening.

I spent some of the set watching the other patrons that were there.
It was apparent they were enthralled by the performance also. There
was also connection of some of the songs to time periods. Fans of Ella

Fitzgerald and Sarah Vaughn were brought back to the time they had first heard those performances or songs. Several of the pop tunes she sang also had a strong time period relationship. The set ended with the singer and band getting enthusiastic applause. It had been a magical performance. A magical performance in a slightly seedy club in a slightly seedy part of town. Leave it to Tony to find this place.

I left shortly thereafter and declined a ride from Tony, feeling a need for a walk to clear my head. It was a nice evening with slightly cool weather. It took me close to an hour to get back to camp. When I did, I found John sitting up reading a book as was his habit. When he saw me, he came to me without saying a word and hugged me. It was awkward and uncomfortable for me. I did my best; I didn't break it off for three full minutes.

I was going to ask him what was up, but I knew he had talked with Lilly. He had told me that morning they had made plans to meet that day. She had probably told him that she wasn't going to have to see the minister anymore. I liked that we were close but the emotions that seemed to bring up were something I wasn't familiar with, comfortable with, and I didn't have a lot of experience with.

After a full three minutes I said, "Alright, alright, what is this, a bucket head's anonymous meeting of huggers?"

We both had a laugh at that.

28

For the next week, I hit two meetings a day to help decompress. I started to get a sense of calm back after a while. I sought Tony out for another chat about my evening with the minister and with the singer and her comments. We went over the same territory about how she could possibly know what transpired between me and the minister. I came up with no new solutions. Talking with Tony about it however helped me let it go. Tony was convinced that I would have no blow back from what happened. He had a very calming effect on me.

I avoided Julie, my AA sponsor, for a bit but after ten days I went to a meeting where I knew I would probably run into her. She asked me point blank why I was avoiding her. So, I told her. I gave her no details but explained I had gotten involved with something that had a good outcome but was violent in its nature. I knew she abhorred violence and I didn't want her to even know about it. The incident was over, and I was getting back on track with my meetings.

After a bit, she simply said, "Well, if there was violence involved, I'm glad it's over."

I told her I didn't want to be involved with any more incidents like this but this one felt important to me.

"I hope it doesn't affect our relationship because you're the main reason I have any sober time," I confessed to her.

She considered that statement for a long moment and finally said, "I think we'll be okay."

I let out a long sigh of relief after she said that and realized how much I was fearing losing her as a sponsor and friend. Julie was magical with her talent of drawing me out and getting me to talk about things I had never even considered talking about. She would ask so many questions that when she was done, I was looking at a situation in a different light. And she always asked me how I felt which was annoying at times but highly beneficial most of the time. I had a sense of how much I needed and benefitted from that. Tony was great but we were not going to discuss our feelings or a lot else really. That was simply the way it was.

29

John was happy. He felt like he had gotten his friend back. He would meet Lilly several times a week after work. They would share their respective days with each other, and it felt a lot like it had before. Lilly had told John that for some reason the minister had suddenly moved away and she was free of him. She asked John if I had anything to do with that. John simply nodded yes but didn't give any more explanation. Truth be known he didn't know any more to give her an explanation.

I settled down after a week or so. I started to believe there would be no repercussions from my adventure with the minister. I also came to realize that I didn't care to have so much emotional turmoil in my life anymore. I craved a quiet, calm existence. I was changing. Being sober changed everything. I couldn't explain that well but knew it had put me in a completely different place.

John's friends Cora and Ekaterina came to town about a week later. They had come to town for a short stay when I had first started program. I had gone to several meetings with them during their stay. They were in program and were staying with a friend of theirs who had an apartment in the area. They lived in another northeast city where John had grown up and I had first met John. That city was about an hour and a half ride by car and had bus and rail connections. It was nice to see them again, especially seeing how they were both sober in program and looked well. They had lost the gaunt look both of them had when I first met them. I suspected a place to stay and regular meals was responsible for that.

Ekaterina was a bit of a tech wiz and was working for the local friend who they were staying with. The friend needed technical and software setup for a business she was involved with. They had gotten together through AA program networking.

Ekaterina seemed to know everything about computers, software, and the history and ins and outs of the internet. She also knew a lot about many other things. She wore it lightly and you had to get to know her a little, but I found out she was scary smart. She spoke perfect English with a very heavy accent. Her mother had moved to the states five years previous for work. She had let a bad relationship and her drinking get in the way of her duties as a mother and the state had put Ekaterina in a foster home four years previous.

Ekaterina had been bounced from foster home to group home for several years before she became a runaway on the streets. It was on the streets she had met Cora who was in a similar situation as her own and had more experience as a runaway. They had bonded as friends and the need to have someone watch the other's back as two young women on the streets.

They had crossed paths with John many times and regarded him as one of a handful of good people also out on the streets. One had to be wary of most people for one reason or another. They had stories galore of their adventures and close calls with violence, psychos, and street thugs. Interestingly enough, they both had gone to NA and AA together and had been clean and sober for a while now. This fact had given their lives a dramatic turn. They were making money, living in an apartment, and looked clean, comfortably dressed, and well fed.

They had rented a bedroom from a friend who was slightly older and could legally rent an apartment. This kept them off the streets and gave them a place to cook and eat. Being smart they both were making money at their respective gigs.

They were considering things like becoming emancipated and declared adults. They sounded and seemed to be on an excellent life track. I met them at day meetings several times during the next week. I joined them for lunch and coffee several times. I found them fun to be around and hang with. Their perspective on things was always educational and thought provoking.

They only allowed me into their somewhat closed world because of my relationship with John. Even the fact that I had saved them from being ripped off and possibly beaten wasn't enough for them to include me. They respected and liked John and at his request they accepted me.

Cora and Ekaterina were very close. I was fascinated at the way they looked out for each other. They were very good friends, and in their situations of being on the streets, good friends was a golden asset. Watching them got me thinking to when I was their age. I tried to think of any relationship that I had that might have been similar. Surely there was someone I was close with that would equate to what they had. I thought about it for a while. I came up empty as unconsciously I knew I would. Empty was how it felt. Empty and something else. After a bit I got it. It made me sad.

I had John in my life, and we were tight. It was probably the closest relationship I had ever had. I had come to really care for John, and I knew he really cared for me. But we weren't teenage friends. I was a mentor and guardian of sorts. I couldn't be a teenage friend of his.

That ship had sailed.

I had been on the streets often at their age. Sometimes with a place to stay and sometimes not. I knew people and sometimes had girlfriends, but I never had a close friend the way Cora and Ekaterina were. It made me jealous and wistful. Sometimes I would see normal things like this and feel mildly shocked that I hadn't had a good friend on the streets. One more simple thing I had missed out on in my life.

I took all this to Julie who was always on me to talk about my feelings. Her thoughts were that we were triggered to drink by the way we felt. She would encourage me to share them with her anytime we were together. Frankly, it felt like a brave new world. A world I was about as comfortable in as a thief in a police station. I had taken her encouragement and suggestions seriously though because I really didn't want to drink anymore.

I met Julie at a meeting and afterwards we went to a coffee shop to talk. I told her about my feelings watching Cora and Ekaterina. She grilled me on my teenage years, looking for connections she thought I might have forgotten about. She was persistent. She asked me again and again about this person I knew or that person I knew. Surely I had someone in the past that would be equivalent. Julie thought I had forgotten at least one someone.

I had hung out with guys for a common need for alcohol or drugs. When I was in grade school there were kids I played sports with but still wasn't tight with. When I got older and started running the streets and drinking nightly, guys were put in categories. Would I end up fighting with this guy or not? Was he someone I had to be concerned with if I did fight him? Did he have any boxing or martial arts skills I needed to be aware of? When I fought him, did he have any friends that would seek payback? I was a very angry teenager and would often find someone to fight with over whatever. For a while it became a lifestyle. Eventually I didn't care about my checklist because I simply wanted to fight.

Julie kept after me looking for a connection that could translate into a real friendship. Coming up empty again and again she started getting frustrated and annoyed with me. Finally I asked, "Julie, do you want me to make someone up?"

Frustrated myself from her questioning I told her friendship would have broken the golden rule I lived by: "You never, under any circumstance, for any reason, let someone get inside your guard. No one gets close. Not for any reason at any time for anything. Period."

I realized that I had just articulated something I never would have defined unless I was grilled by someone the way Julie had grilled me. I looked at Julie after coming up with this explanation and found her looking at me with tears in her eyes. She said, "Damn, even when I was turning tricks on the streets to get high, I had a friend or two I could count on."

I just looked at Julie who was so appalled by the fact that I didn't have friends she was crying. Apparently, this wasn't normal in her eyes. Until today it was something I had never considered or thought about. I was baffled at her reaction, but I could tell it was something I would think about for some time. Feel your feelings, I was told. *Gee, wasn't this fun?*

30

Why didn't I have friends? The question was on my mind several days later when I was alone having a coffee in a restaurant after a meeting. I had a pen and a small notebook on which I started jotting down names of grade school acquaintances. I quickly realized having a friend come over to the house was out of the question when my father was home and a dubious challenge with my mother also. My father was always drunk, critical, and morose. My mother was occasionally sociable but could change in a heartbeat into an angry person who would do or say something embarrassing. On top of that, the drunken relatives could come over at any time and drink with my parents, which often would turn into a huge argument with occasional fisticuffs. The bottom line was, as a young boy, I was afraid to have anyone come over the house. I was mortified on the few occasions when a friend from class had come by and witnessed drunken insanity. I would worry for weeks after that. Someone in my class at school would know all my shame because one of them had witnessed something.

The house situation was only part of it though. I really never did let anybody in. I never talked about my home or the house with anyone. As a young boy the common denominator was sports and if you were any good. Also, if you could run fast. It was constant seasonal sports after school straight 'til dinnertime.

In fourth grade my father started hitting my mother. I would jump in between them and catch a beating for my troubles. Then I would have the embarrassment of coming up with a story for the black eye or fat lip I'd have. I never told anyone the truth about those beatings.

In the fifth grade I started fighting, and when I got a black eye or a fat lip it was a relief to have my classmates know that I had earned them in a fight. Then the truth wasn't an embarrassment. I liked fighting whether I won or lost. I was usually wound up like a top when a fight would present itself to me and I would relish the release. I had a lot of built-up rage to fuel these events because if I got beat on and knocked down, I would get up an inordinate number of times no matter how bloody I got.

Ma on occasion would get upset when I came home bloodied and bruised. My father would just look at me with disdain and say, "I hope you gave as good as you got." Thinking about this now for the first time made me aware that these weren't parent of the year statements to an eleven-year-old child.

The upside was that by the time I got to the ninth grade, I had a reputation as being crazy enough to fight long past the stage of where most fights would wind down with a winner and loser. The occurrence of physical pain from a fight gave me fuel and desire to continue. Later on, I would try to end fights without getting hit but in the beginning it felt good. It felt like bliss. It was permission to hit someone and feel a release.

Julie's questions and reaction to my childhood opened up a Pandora's box of memories for me. Not about friends like she was searching for but about fights. A seeming endless number of fights. My life as a teenager was filled with constant battles.

The streets I ran and the schools I went to were full of angry boys who served as a constant supply of fight participants. A perceived slight was all it would take to set things off. It got to a point I didn't have to go through the bother of pretending there was a slight. I could look at another kid and just know we were on. Right there, right then it was time to fight. Memories came back of fight after fight. No rhyme, no reason, we had sought each other out knowing we were out there and there would be a fight. We would circle each other and size each other up for a moment or two before the fists flew. Thinking about it now, I was startled how often I fought and how violent my life was. I was suspended from middle and high school eight or more times before I was finally expelled.

By high school I was using my house as a crash pad only. I had a girlfriend whose mother took a liking to me who would have me over for dinner on a regular basis. She at times would let me crash there and sleep on the couch. I fell out of favor with her and others because I was constantly hurt or showing some physical sign of damage from the lifestyle.

In the middle of my reverie about my teenage fighting career I had a revelation that stunned me. I remembered that I actually had had a friend. His name was Sean. We had been tight in seventh grade. We played a lot of basketball on the local courts in Southie. If one court was barren, we would run a mile or two to another court to look for a good game. Different courts had different activities going on at different times. We would try to find a good game to be involved with. On occasion we would shoot baskets alone and play one-on-one games with each other.

On these occasions I would get to know Sean a little. He came from a single parent house and had four siblings whom he would rarely talk about. He would intimate difficult situations at home. Not talk about them but reference them in a backhanded sort of way. For a couple of young tough Irish kids that was serious communication.

One day after such an intimation I told him my father was a serious drunk. That was it. That was all I said. Growing up in Southie I felt that more need not be said. Sean commiserated with me and said, "That really sucks."

After that we sat on a bench drinking sodas we had brought with us, watching the sun go down and basking in an air of friendship. I remembered that moment distinctly because it was the only time I had ever felt close to someone who may have been a friend. He disappeared shortly thereafter.

Later I heard that he had started drinking and drugging with a vengeance in eighth grade. He died by suicide at seventeen. I ran into a mutual acquaintance a year or so after who bluntly stated he was fallout from one of the priests that the Globe's spotlight series had unveiled. Peter, the mutual acquaintance, had a brother who was abused, and he was really angry and bitter about it. He named the priest who he believed abused Sean and named two other victims of mutually known local kids.

I was shocked and enraged hearing that. I never really processed it and got busy with the insanity of my life and my illustrious drinking career.

The thought of Sean and his life made me feel unbelievably sad. If I knew how to cry, I would've. But I didn't. So I sat there feeling sad and lost and alone.

There was one upside, I thought. I could tell Julie that I had had a friend. I had remembered one friend from my youth. It might make her feel better. It might make me feel almost human.

31

When I was a sophomore in high school, I discovered a gym that taught boxing. One of my drunk uncles signed me up for lessons there after he repeatedly saw me with bruises. He probably thought I was losing fights all the time. Fact was I seldom lost; on my way to victory though there was a certain amount of carnage inflicted on me. One day in a semi-inebriated state he insisted I come with him to a nearby gym where they taught boxing lessons.

He paid for three months of lessons in advance for me. A week later he wanted some of his money back, but it was too late. There were no refunds. I was glad for that because I was already hooked on the gym. I learned how to hit a speed bag and would do constant rounds between the speed and the heavy bag.

After three months I scraped up enough money to go another three months. My constant work on the bags got me noticed by one of the boxing coaches who started teaching me. He started with just showing me how to throw a punch. He then would put on pads and have me work on combinations of three and five punches.

I loved the gym. I loved the training. I loved the grind of the routines. Speed bags, heavy bag, jump rope. Then the ring work. Hit the pads with practiced combinations and then as the coach called out different punches. Then eventually sparring with others. Work and sweat. Work and sweat. Blissful.

I was good too. Driven and compulsive I picked up skills quickly. By the time I was seventeen I was considered a favorite in the middle-weight division of the local Golden Gloves competition.

Alcohol messed that up. I had drunk previously, but gave it up mostly for six months when I found the gym. It creeped back in my life. A couple of times I had a few social drinks on the weekend which turned out okay. One day I drank because I was primed after a visit to my home.

My mother had a bruise on her cheek, and I confronted my father over it. He was pretty drunk and told me to fuck off. For the first time in my life, I hit him. My mother screamed at me for hitting him. I was attempting to defend her, and she was mad at me over it. I stormed off into the night. I got my hands on a bottle of whiskey and got drunk and passed out on a bench in a small nearby park.

When I came to it was almost dawn and I felt very cold. I snuck into the cellar of an uncle's house. There I slept for another six hours. When I woke up, I was hungover, miserable, confused, and homeless. There was no way I was going back to my house. There seemed to be only one answer for my condition and that was another drink. I started with some beers that I had and bought myself another bottle of cheap whiskey to get obliterated. I walked around town and stopped and drank for a bit in a dive bar that was known to be lenient with I.D.s. The fake I.D. that I used was poor with someone else's picture on it. Here it was good enough.

With my previous drinking and a few more shots I was feeling no pain. I ordered another round and waited. I was raging inside, and the booze was just fueling it rather than calming it down. I had never hit my father before and I felt bad about that. Then I would think about how he hit my mother and I'd want to hit him again. Then I would get mad at my mother for yelling at me for basically defending her. Then I felt guilty about that.

The short time I had spent home had made me insane. And I knew I couldn't live there anymore so I was homeless. I was a mix of anger, shame, guilt, confusion, terror, and rage. The booze was acting like an accelerant for all those feelings.

I didn't have to wait too long. God bless dive bars. There was always trouble brewing somewhere. Five or six local kids came in for their drinks after work. They were blue collared kids and considered themselves local tough guys. I never remembered what set it off, but I was not surprised it was set off. Words were exchanged and the insults started. Game time.

I laid into the group with fury and purpose. I was close to putting four out of action when one of them caught me on the temple with a pool stick. I managed to fight on for a bit, but I was dizzy, woozy, and felt nauseous from the head blow. More sticks were acquired, and the fight went south for me. I was knocked unconscious and woke up in the ICU of the local hospital emergency room. I had a serious concussion and three broken ribs, a broken nose and multiple contusions and bruises everywhere. I spent two weeks in the hospital because of the brain injury.

The doctors had to relieve pressure from my brain several times because I had something called intracranial brain pressure caused by the multiple blows to the head. The doctors drilled a hole in my head to alleviate the pressure. I was a mess. I heard later that once I hit the floor in that bar the locals had a field day on my limp form. They rained blows down on me for a while before they felt satiated. The doctors told me a couple more blows to the head probably would have done me in.

I needed time to heal because I was bruised and contused everywhere on my body. It hurt to move at all. My physical condition was the easy part to deal with though. My mother came by after two days and never mentioned my last visit to the house. She had faint vestiges of a black eye that hadn't completely healed. I was going to ask her about it but figured, what was the use? She would only lie, and there was nothing I could do about it anyway.

When she left, I knew one thing for sure: I couldn't go home. It wasn't home for me anymore. I wondered if it ever was. I couldn't ignore the elephant in the living room anymore. I couldn't pretend that what I saw was okay. I would lose it on a daily basis if I continued to live there. I had to find somewhere else to live.

The beating also ended my boxing career. It was six months before I went back to the boxing gym. It was another six months after that before I was cleared to spar with anybody. I could work out there but had to wait a full year to get clearance on my concussion. I would do some sparring and still loved the workout but by then I was drinking much more and couldn't muster the discipline to be a serious fighter. I couldn't not drink. I broke one of the coach's hearts. He really believed in my talent and potential. After a while I stopped going to that gym because I couldn't bear the disappointment he seemed to have when he saw me.

32

For the next three days I went to several meetings a day after my reveries about the past. My memories brought up a lot of feelings which for me was difficult and uncomfortable. This in the past was where a drink would come in. That was no longer an option. I was under strict instructions from Julie to stay close to meetings and her when I had a lot of feelings going on. Julie was the perfect sponsor for me. She was wise beyond her years. She not only knew the program but also had great intuition of what people were going through and needed.

I couldn't think of another person in AA that I knew that I would actually listen to. She presented things in a way that I would do what she suggested. I needed that. I didn't know why but I was grateful.

I told her about remembering that I had had a friend. I hadn't wanted to continue the story, but she kept asking me what happened to him and where was he now. I told her. She looked at me with great sadness. It made me wish I hadn't told her. I realized I had told her because I wanted to have something that proved or indicated I was normal, like friends. Then I thought, *I'm trying to get a normal life status from a woman who had been a prostitute as a teenager. What, pray tell, did that say about me?* I needed to stop thinking so I went to another meeting.

33

I would see John every day, but we were starting to live such separate lives that we became like two ships in the night. He would go to work with Tony. He was saving some money and would hang out with his friends during his free time. I was often at a meeting and hanging with Julie or someone else from the program.

I missed him and told him so one night in camp. I said we need to get together and hang out. He asked me what I wanted to do. I told him I didn't really care as long as we were together. He told me to hang on and called Tony and arranged to take the next day off from work. He then asked if I would go fishing with him. I said sure but warned him that I didn't know the first thing about fishing. He said that was okay and he knew how to fish and where to go. Also, Tony had some fishing gear we could borrow.

The next day we got up early and headed toward Tony's place to borrow fishing gear for the day. Along the way we stopped and had some breakfast at a restaurant. I asked him about his work with Tony and he told me about the projects they were involved with. Tony would now have several jobs going on at once and had hired another guy who was a carpenter to help. John seemed to really like working and learning what he could from Tony and the new carpenter. I was happy to hear that.

When we got to Tony's house, John produced a key for the barn that Tony had. John went inside and procured a couple of fishing poles. He went back in and came out with a tackle box full of lures and hooks and other fishing things. I noticed the BMW motorcycle still half apart and asked John if Tony had made any headway fixing it up. John said he didn't think so because Tony had a dozen projects going on at once. John locked up the barn and we headed to a lake that he knew about where we could go fishing.

I had to laugh at the two of us with our fishing poles and tackle box. We looked like a couple of characters out of Mayberry. I had to admit I was enjoying myself. I thought about that and after a moment I got it. It felt like I was having fun. At least what I thought of what fun was. In the past, the only way I could let go to feel anything akin to fun was to drink a lot. The drunkenness and hangover and despair that came with the drinking usually ruined that mood.

I felt an intense desire to tell Julie I had discovered another feeling. She had noted that I had a limited emotional range. I wanted to tell her I had discovered what fun is. A part of me wanted to get acknowledgement from her that yes, that was another feeling and yes, I was becoming normal. I decided that I wasn't going to ruin this day with my constant ruminations about everything. I had to stop with the incessant thinking. At least for today.

I focused on John and asked him about his friend Lilly: how she was doing and if he still met her in the park. He told me he had seen her the day before and she was doing better. He went on to say that she was still a little sad at times which John didn't like to see but didn't know what to do about. I told him that just being there and being her friend was a big deal and a wonderful thing.

"She needs time to recover from the abuse the minister put her through."

"She thanks me every time I see her for whatever you did to stop the minister," he said after going quiet for a moment. "What did you do to stop him so abruptly?" he asked.

"Why, I simply made him an offer he couldn't refuse."

John looked at me quizzically and I realized the Godfather reference was a poor choice.

"You're not going to tell me what you did, are you?"

I looked at him and said, "Do not take this personally, but no I am not going to tell you what I did. That will stay between me and the minister and God."

I was glad he let that go and we talked about other things on our way to Mayberry. When we got to the lake, John led me into the woods that surrounded much of the lake and led us to a nice spot where there was a boulder that extended into the lake we could fish off. It was a beautiful day. Sunny and warm with no humidity. John seemed to know his way around the fishing gear and gave me some running commentary on the different types of lures and what the best use of each of them was. He struggled a little tying them on to the fishing line but eventually he got the job done.

He gave me a decent tutorial on the workings of the reel. In a short time, we were sitting there with our hook and lines in the water fishing. I asked him where he had learned how to use the fishing gear. He told me mostly from Tony. He had fished a few times with a foster father, but Tony had taken him out several times when they had finished their work early. Tony knew about all the freshwater ponds in and around the city where one could fish.

John asked me about Tony and how we came to be friends. I told him about our bonding at the bar drinking after our little bar fight. He shook his head wistfully saying, "I would have loved to have been a fly on the wall to see that fight."

We talked about Tony for a bit. I realized I hadn't seen him in a while either. He went to different meetings than I did so I didn't run into him often at AA. I asked John how he was doing and if he was still seeing his new girlfriend, Beth. Then I remembered he was going to propose to her and have a party soon. John said he was doing good and that he had proposed and was now engaged. I asked about her. John said he had met her, and she was really nice, and he thought Tony was in love with her.

Wow, Tony in love. I was happy to hear that. Tony was a loner, and I thought a wife was a positive thing in his life.

"I hope she is not as homely as Tony?" I asked.

John laughed at that question and reassured me that indeed she was not homely at all but was somewhat pretty.

"I wasn't dissing Tony by that statement."

John chuckled and said, "I didn't think you were, but you're right; if she was as homely as Tony, we'd all be in trouble."

We both laughed at that.

John got a bite on his line and after a bit he reeled in a decent sized Perch. After going fishing with Tony, he had acquired a book on the subject and had learned about the different varieties of fish. I told him he seemed like a real pro with his knowledge of the gear and the fish. I was impressed and told him so.

The day stayed beautiful, and we sat in the sun with our poles on the rock in the woods, fishing in the lake. I couldn't think of another place in the world I'd rather be than right there right then. That felt different but also nice.

John also seemed happy which made it especially nice for me. My feelings for John scared me. It was a whole new world. It felt loaded with pitfalls and booby traps and pain. It made me feel vulnerable and that was something I had tried to avoid my whole life. I had talked with Julie about this many times since I started back at meetings. She would tell me feeling vulnerable was okay. She also thought that both John and I had a better life because of our relationship. She would ask if my chances of staying sober were better or worse with John around. Then she would ask if I knew how much John worshipped me. I told her I had a sense of that, and I liked that fact but really didn't know if it was a good or a bad thing. She would insist that it was a good thing.

I had done it again. I was messing up the day by thinking too much. It made me wish I had a knob somewhere on my body I could turn to make my brain stop. But I didn't so I focused on the bob that was above my fishing hook and watched for movement. I was rewarded after a few minutes with some action. I had a fish on my line. It was a decent size fish judging from the fight it was putting up.

I asked John, "How do I reel the fish in?"

I spent the next ten minutes reeling him in a little at a time, following John's instructions. I was rewarded by landing a fourteen-inch rainbow trout which was considered a big fish in this lake. It was a pretty fish and was a gratifying moment. I realized I had never been fishing before, so this was the first fish I ever caught. John was excited and made me hold up the fish while he snapped a picture with his phone. After that we put the fish back in the lake and let him go.

John caught and released four more fish during the next two hours. I couldn't think or see what he was doing different to get most of the action, so I asked him if he was cheating somehow or hadn't told me something noteworthy.

He laughed and said, "Maybe you just suck at fishing."

Actually, I still felt very gratified and excited over my one big catch. After catching his fifth fish we broke out some sandwiches and chips we had bought on the way to the lake. After we finished John asked me if I had thought anymore about adopting him and getting a place we could live in. John had asked me about doing that about a month prior.

I told him I had thought about it a lot and liked the idea, but it was predicated on me staying sober, getting a job, making some money, and getting my own place.

"You might be eighteen by the time I accomplish all that."

I hadn't made a firm decision, but I decided then and there and told John that I would work towards all of that. I also emphasized his hopes were on a person who may or may not stop drinking and that could be a recipe for disappointment for him.

John said he didn't care and still couldn't get over what I had done for Lilly. He asked me if I would do that for him.

I pondered that a moment and quietly stated, "I did do that for you. Did you forget how we met?"

John sat there with his fishing pole and started to silently weep. After a bit I put my arm around his shoulders, and we sat in the sun on the rock in the woods with our poles fishing in the lake.

34

I felt panicked for the next week about all the things I had promised to do involving John. Julie and several other program people talked me down and I started to see how I tortured myself with anxiety. It didn't change the anxiety, but I found if I could talk to someone, preferably Julie, I could get some relief. One of the primary slogans for a newcomer was constantly thrown at me. Easy does it. A simple concept that seemed impossible to follow with my mindset and emotional makeup. But I did start to talk about it.

Priority one was not drinking because if I drank all the other goals would melt away like the snow in April. Number two would be to get a place to stay. Fall had begun and winter was coming. Julie had me focusing on staying sober, getting to meetings, and believing the rest would take care of itself. Simple but a semi-impossible concept for me to grasp. Although when she reminded me, I found it helpful.

Work was an issue. What could I actually do to make a living going forward? I did not have confidence in having a strong constitution that could allow me to work the way I once had. I had worked in construction rough framing houses for a builder in the past. I had also worked many different types of construction, working out of a union hall for different companies. I had liked the physical nature of the work which had also helped with hangovers.

All of this adult, real shit was making me crazy. Sue crossed my mind. I thought if I could get with her, I could forget about life stuff for a few hours. I borrowed a phone and gave her a call. When she heard my voice, she let me have it.

"Where the hell have you been and why haven't you called to at least let me know you're around and okay?"

On and on she went. I let her vent. When she was done, I stayed quiet not knowing quite what to say and not wanting to say the wrong thing. There was a long pause. Finally, with nothing else coming to mind, I simply asked, "Are you feeling stressed?"

It was the only thing that came to mind. Apparently, it was the right thing. She fell out laughing. Eventually she gathered herself and said yes and told me to be at her place in thirty minutes. I was about forty minutes away and I realized this was the time to focus on things. I was successful. I made it in twenty-eight.

She wasn't kidding. When I got there, she threw me in the shower after which she kept me busy for some time.

It was busy work. I didn't mind though. What was interesting was she hadn't drunk, and of course neither had I. It was the second time we had sex sober. When we had first met, we had started the relationship with both of us feeling no pain. Having sex without having drank was new to me and maybe to her too. I asked her about it afterward. She turned the question around and asked me if I liked it better. I told her I did.

"It's different to remember all of it."

She told me her sex life was probably 50 percent drinking and 50 percent not drinking. She was a little surprised to hear my statistics of two times sober and the rest under the influence. I told her, this being the second time, I was starting to warm up to it. We relaxed for a bit afterwards. She let me smoke out on the balcony outside her bedroom. After a bit she told me she needed to ask me something serious. I looked at her quizzically.

She asked, "What kind of numbers do we need to make a fifty-fifty ratio of sober sex for you?"

I said I didn't know but I would ponder the question while we worked toward parity.

35

I tried to meet with my sponsor Julie often. She knew about my relationship with John and what I hoped to do. She shared some about her early sobriety when everything looked impossible and how, a day at a time, everything became possible. She had a remarkable story. She stated how it didn't make any sense but the thing that helped her the most was to simply surrender to going to a lot of meetings. It was the only way she could let go of all the "shoulds" and perfectionistic way of thinking that she had and also heard from me when I talked with her.

She shared that by simply going to meetings everything else actually did take care of itself. I told her I'd have to think on that as it was not something I could wrap my mind around.

We made plans to get together the following Saturday. It was hard to get time alone with Julie after a meeting because she had other people she sponsored and was a very popular person in recovery. Everybody wanted to talk with her. I appreciated being able to occasionally get together alone and talk. It was during those times that her calm, thoughtful questioning and wisdom would draw me out in ways that I couldn't even begin to describe.

Recently Julie had been telling me she experienced me as being depressed. She would like to see me be assessed by a psychiatrist. She had told me this after a meeting where I didn't have time ask her about it. The statement was adding to my stress. I didn't have health insurance. The options for the homeless and indigent were talked about on the street in less than stellar ways.

The problem was that I thought she was right. I thought I was depressed. I had read about drinking as medication for depression. Medication that didn't work of course. Now that I wasn't drinking, I sometimes felt a bone-weary tiredness at times.

Julie had questioned me on what I had been doing the last eight years. Whereas I was living the life and times of an alcoholic; the last three years had really stuck out. During those years I had lived more isolated and alone than usual. Usually, I was already isolated and alone so that was saying something. My interactions with other people grew less and less. I had gotten to the point that getting food, cigarettes, and booze were the only times I interacted with people. Occasionally I worked. But even those gigs had been doing isolated labor of a sort where I didn't have to interact with anybody. I had become comfortable with it without being aware I was doing it.

I also had remembered something. I had become suicidal. I had been fighting a losing battle with suicidal thoughts. The constant self-criticism I lived with had turned into an evil mantra of self-destruction.

Kill yourself, kill yourself. What's the point of living? You have no money; you have no purpose; what's the point? Everybody else has a life but you. You have no family; you have no purpose; kill yourself, kill yourself.

The mantra would go on and on. The relentless nature of the thoughts and the seeming endless array of negativity about my life that would back up the voice was more than a little frightening. I remembered I had actually thought about having to do something soon. What, I didn't know, but something.

The accelerating mental deterioration had been interrupted. John had come along. Since meeting John, I had dealt with constant situations with other people. Never mind living with John. My drinking had gotten worse and then I had met Julie. The one person in the world I would actually listen to and heed their advice. I might not follow her advice, but I would consider it. She was good too. Anybody who could draw me out despite my tightlipped Irish Catholic upbringing was gifted. I would rather you pull all my fingernails out than tell you how I really felt. I lived on a need-to-know basis. And mostly always you didn't need to know.

Getting around forty generations of Irish Catholic repression was no easy feat. *This*, I thought, *should be investigated as a miracle*. It also made me extremely grateful for Julie, and more than a little in awe.

Saturday came and I met Julie for brunch in a local restaurant. I asked about her work. Did she like being a lawyer? Was the job in the Attorney General's office a good gig? She told me she loved being a lawyer and that yes, working in the AG's office was a good gig. She felt she was getting lots of good experience and had the chance to work in a variety of areas on a variety of cases.

Every day was a chance to learn something new and exciting about the law and the role the law played in society. I asked her if she felt her life was stressful with her schedule and all. She laughed, saying she didn't find it stressful at all.

Before graduation the previous May, she had been going to school full-time, studying constantly to pass tests and do papers, working almost full-time, and going to meetings and trying to stay sober.

"That was stressful," she said. "I didn't feel like I ever had time to relax. Now I'm just working and going to meetings. I'm busy but it's manageable. The real stress was when I was drinking. The hangovers, the wanting to score coke to accent my drinking, and then succumbing to selling myself to pay for it. Then the self-loathing and self-hatred and then a drink and then the coke and then the tricks and the humiliation." Her voiced tailed off. She looked at me and continued, "You've been working really hard to keep drinking, and you're probably like I was with no awareness of it. I had to be sober for some time to put together how much work drinking was."

I considered that and said, "I may not be aware, but the thought of drinking makes me feel exhausted. I'm aware of how exhausted I feel after binging for a day or three."

After a pause, she sighed and said, "I'm very glad to hear you feel that way. I don't think you realize the part you played in my sobriety. Not really anyway. When I came in, I was such a mess and the fact that I had been prostituting myself just killed me when I thought of a higher power. I could not believe a God would have anything to do with me. You were the one that convinced me otherwise. You were the one that gave me hope that I was worth something and that I could get sober. And if I got sober I could and would feel better about myself. You were very convincing to me. You felt like a guardian angel at that time and then you introduced me to Jennifer; a wonderful woman who still is my sponsor.

"Do you remember any of this?" she queried.

I told her I did remember a little and thought I had been helpful. However, I didn't realize I had that big an impact.

"Then I had the incident where one of the newcomers in AA who had been a client of mine when I was out there was giving me a hard time," she said. "He would ask me things like 'How's tricks Julie?' And he would do that in front of other AA members. I couldn't handle that at that time. I was mortified. I was on the verge of leaving AA when you stopped that. Somebody went to bat for me. Somebody stuck up for me! Somebody defended my reputation when I thought I was worthless. And a guy no less who wasn't looking for something from me. And especially not looking for sex from me. Do you remember that?"

"Yes, I remember that! I had always wondered if you had found out about that."

"Yes, I found out about that and heard details from four different people."

Damn, I thought, *anonymity doesn't extend itself too far sometimes.*

Julie had never liked violence and defending her honor that evening, I had gotten violent. Which was why I was wary and a bit afraid of her finding out. Shortly after that I had stopped going to meetings and never found out if Julie had heard about it.

I had come out of a meeting one night and was smoking and chatting with a friend when I overheard the raucous ribaldry of a guy talking about a woman. I heard Julie's name mentioned. She had shared at the meeting so everyone who was listening knew who he was talking about. He gave a description of the sex he had with her and wondered out loud to a bunch of guys if he could still pay and get the sex again.

That being a polite description of what I had overheard, I felt that I was working my program in that I didn't hit him immediately. I walked over, taking several deep breaths, trying to calm myself, and squared off with the guy.

"Why don't we give the woman a break and shut the fuck up? We all led different lives before AA."

He wasn't having it and came back with, "How about you leave before I make you my bitch?"

He started to continue while I slowly started turning to my right like I was leaving but came back with serious speed on a right cross, catching him squarely on the jaw. It was a move and a punch I had perfected over the years in countless fights. I had found if I could connect with the jaw the fight was over. The fight was over, but I wasn't done. I walked over to him struggling to get up and kicked him full out in the stomach, which put him back on the pavement. I bent over, pushing his head into the sand on the asphalt and grinding his face into it.

After a minute, my rage cooled and I said, "If I ever hear that you talked about Julie again, I will make this seem like a fun night out for you."

When I stood up there was a bit of a crowd of people who had been at the meeting standing around. I took a moment to look the crowd over to see if someone who he was friends with might come at me. I didn't see anyone who appeared to be a threat, so I simply walked away.

Shortly thereafter I had relapsed. I had forgotten about the incident as it was just one in a long history of fights I had been in. I hadn't thought about it much until today, until Julie had brought it up. I was relieved to find that she had heard about it, and she wasn't angry about it.

Julie continued with, "The reason I'm going over all of this with you is would you have imagined me here sober, working, a lawyer no less, when you knew me from back then?"

I chuckled and admitted I never would have pictured her looking and being the woman I saw in front of me.

"Exactly. Which is precisely why I want you to look at and listen to me. I am living visual proof of what I'm telling you. I had nothing when I came into sobriety. Nothing. Not only did I have nothing, but I had no idea I could have a life or know what I wanted to do if I did have a life. I had no aspirations for college and didn't realize I was smart enough to go to college and do as well as I did. I had health issues, no money, no prospects, and I couldn't stop drinking, drugging, or turning tricks. When I came into the halls of AA, you and Jennifer and others told me to not worry. If I stayed sober, all the things I was worrying about would take care of themselves and I would be alright. That turned out to be true. I didn't need to worry about housing and food and what was I going to do for work. I didn't need to worry about all the health concerns I had. I didn't need to worry about the future. I needed to go to a meeting, stay sober and clean, and begin to live in the day."

"That is what you need to do. All these other concerns that you are feeling pressure about are secondary to your simple objective of not drinking and going to a meeting. They may seem of primary importance, but they are not. If you focus on not drinking and meetings, somehow those other concerns and needs will be met in ways much better than you could have imagined."

"Of course, being human, I didn't quite believe any of that and I worried at a good clip. I am trying to save you a lot of that by convincing you of what I know to be true even if I learned it in hindsight. Do you get what I'm saying?"

I told her yes, I understood what she was saying but I found it next to impossible to believe that if I went to a meeting that my health concerns, housing concerns, work concerns, and concerns about my promises with John would all be taken care of.

Julie sighed and admitted it was a tall order to swallow. Then she went on for another thirty minutes telling me about the many little miracles that happened to her after she got into the program. Jobs, housing, scholarships for school, healers who helped her with health conditions. She had a litany of instances of her higher power's help that she believed occurred because of her involvement in the program.

I was impressed by her pitch and caring. I didn't completely buy it, but I was listening and understood her premise. I told her how much I appreciated her care for me which was palpable and meant the world. She admitted she hated being powerless over people and really, really wanted me to stay sober and reap the benefits of so doing.

She had tears in her eyes when she said this. I looked at her feeling moved in places that had been long dormant. I wondered if this interaction was what one would call the grace of God? I felt loved by Julie. It brought up fear. It moved me and brought up feelings. Feelings I may have had at one time but now felt uncomfortable.

Feelings made me fearful. I had them once but had learned to repress them. I was shamed for feelings as a young boy. I got good

at stuffing them and burying them deep. Yet here they were again.
Julie would tell me that my feelings wouldn't kill me. Maybe not but
I would almost rather die than feel them. Even love was extremely
uncomfortable. The love I felt from Julie. If I kept feeling this, would
I cry? If I cried, would I ever be able to stop? That sort of vulnerability, I wasn't ready for. I took a breath and distracted myself with an
odd thought. The feelings subsided. I was relieved but also strangely
disappointed.

36

Tony had a cookout. He had a lot to celebrate. He was sober for a year again which was a notable milestone for him. He would celebrate at his next home group meeting but was having a cookout this weekend. He invited friends of his and his new fiancée Beth. When I got to his house, the cookout was in full swing. John was already there because he had helped Tony prep for the cookout. John's friends Cora and Ekaterina were there also. There were a dozen or so program people and other friends of Tony's there. I knew many of them from meetings.

I met Beth and we had a chat. I was impressed. She was warm and friendly and seemed happy with Tony. As John had told me she was also pretty. I felt happy for Tony with Beth in his life. I had known him to be with a woman here or there but never in a relationship. Certainly, never with a person as warm and friendly as Beth. Tony seemed to radiate happiness when he was near her. John was right; Tony was in love.

The day was warm and sunny. A perfect day for a cookout. There was a volleyball net set up on the side of the house. There was a three-on-three game of volleyball going on. There was a horseshoe pit in the back of the house. A handful of people were standing around watching a couple of guys throw against each other. Tony was holding court by the grill where he presided over the cooking and directed people to beverages and food that was laid out on a long table. John was busy getting things from the kitchen or various coolers as needed. People were sitting on lawn chairs here and there talking and laughing. People came and went and came back again. It was an idyllic day. I found an empty recliner and napped in the sun for a few minutes, after which I grabbed some food and ate my share and maybe a little more. People had brought quite a bit of food, and nobody needed to go hungry.

I reflected on cookouts we had when I was a kid. By now the booze would be in effect and an argument here or there would have broken out. Family resentments and feuds would be starting to be laid bare and a fight would have to be broken up. Chaos and anger and bullshit with my dad and uncles would end up ruining the day. I would take off and avoid as much as I could. Then later on I might get a beating for having taken off.

This cookout had no booze and everyone seemed happy. Tony and Beth were surrounded by people they knew and liked. Everyone was content with the day and the food and the volleyball and the horseshoes and the conversations that broke out here and there and everywhere. It was seductive. Despite my inclination not to I joined in. I conversed with many people I knew from the program. I ran into a few people I knew from my first time around eight years previous. A couple of them had stayed the course but I found out several had relapsed like me and were back with a short amount of time. We discussed the fact we had found no answers in the booze and were glad we were sober again.

Cora and Ekaterina were holding court at one of the tables set up in the yard. A small crowd was milling about when I walked over to join them. Cora was telling stories about panhandling on the street and the different reactions she got from people when asked for money.

It ran the gamut from disgust to generosity and real care. It also led to interactions with boys and men looking for sex. That led to another host of stories about men and their particular dangers.

Cora added, "But not all men," and started to tell a story about a rude young businessman who had insulted her and Ekaterina. She went on saying that a man came out of nowhere grabbed the guy and made the man apologize to them. I was so absorbed in her stories and the humorous way she presented them it took me a moment to realize she was talking about me. She looked over at me and said, "Here is the man of the hour in person."

I blushed a little with her putting the spotlight on me.

Someone asked, "So this is the guy you were telling us about?"

Cora nodded her head. "Yes, it is."

John chimed in with, "Cora called me shortly thereafter and told me the story and I knew it was him."

I started hoping he wasn't going to get into how we had met. Mercifully the stories about me stopped there. I was always uncomfortable when people put a spotlight on me for either good or bad reasons. With my recent new awareness from talking with Julie I knew there was probably a reason for this and made a mental note to talk to her about it. That feeling was complex though. A part of me liked the notoriety but another part of me hated the attention. At any rate, the story telling was picked up by Ekaterina who also had some Russian tales as well as American. Stories about street life and being a runaway in Moscow.

Both Cora and Ekaterina were solidly in the program and had groups and sponsors and lots of program friends. I could see if they stayed sober, they might have the type of success that Julie had. They were both extremely bright and I could easily see them going to college in the near future.

As I was thinking that I had a fearful thought that sent shivers up my spine. The nebulous nature of sobriety. If they stayed sober. That was a hell of an if and nobody knew more than me the minefields and lack of guarantees. I wasn't the only one who went out after start-ing sobriety. I was lucky to have made it back. I had grown fond of them though. Plus they were good friends of John's and John thought highly of their friendship. I hoped they would make it.

37

Life went on as it does. Another day and then another. I took Julie's advice and went to meetings daily. I was trying to stay in the moment but realized I was still doing more than a little worrying about my prospects in the future. Where was I going to live? What could I do for work? Julie had also given me another thing to worry about. Was I depressed? Was my constant tiredness and lack of energy to do things always going to be here? I tried not to dwell on those things but found it hard.

Now I had a reason to care. I had told John if I could, I would become his guardian. That meant I had to do things to make that happen. Things that really seemed impossible with the way I felt. It was extremely frustrating. I tried to talk about it at meetings. People would react to my sharing in a way that stopped me from sharing. They would tell me how they had gone through something similar that wasn't really similar. Or they would tell me how God would take care of things which was a belief I was really struggling with. It took all of my willpower to not tell them to shut the fuck up.

I would get together with Julie once a week or so. I found that I could vent and decompress with her. I told her about my reactions to people at meetings. I asked why I always felt so angry and pissed off at everybody, especially since ostensibly they were trying to help me. She explained that they may mean well but when people made comments to her like that in early sobriety, she would feel like she wasn't really feeling heard. She said she was really sensitive to that and apparently, I was also.

"In early sobriety I had Jennifer, another friend named Rose, and you to listen to me. That was it. Other people would make me feel the same as you're feeling. You guys made me feel heard. I stopped trying to be heard by others. I stuck with people who were good for me. Besides, since I've known you, your whole emotional life has revolved around anger," she said. "You're learning to talk about things and feel other feelings, but you've just started that process. Obviously you're comfortable talking to me, and in time you'll find a few others that can validate and hear you in a way that is satisfying."

She explained that there are all kinds of people in AA as in any organization. AA has its share of controlling people.

"This is what is meant by principles above personalities."

I was grateful for Julie. She could always take me off the latest emotional cliff I found myself on. She also had a way of turning esoteric platitudes I knew or had heard into an example that made it real for me. Without a way to vent or decompress I had a hard time seeing myself staying in program. I may still feel like hitting people, but I really didn't want to drink anymore. Julie was my lifeline.

I was introduced to the world of halfway houses. Or at least the possibility of one. The community had a halfway house where one could live when newly sober. Availability of beds was an issue, but I got an intake appointment that would enable me to get on a list for a bed. There were a number of rules and requirements one had to abide by if you lived there but the ones I had heard of seemed doable.

Other services were also available through the halfway house. Things like counseling and an assessment for depression were intimated as possibilities. There were people in the meetings that were involved with the halfway house that had described these things to me and helped me get an intake appointment. I had used Julie as a reference which seemed to help me get the appointment. She was known and respected in this circle of people.

If I went inpatient somewhere, there was the issue of where and whom John would live with. I had some ideas about that but decided I'd cross that bridge when I got there.

John was continuing to stay busy with his work for Tony. I had met Tony for dinner and a meeting one night and he told me that he was happy to have the extra work as he felt he needed the money. There was a reason. Tony wanted to get married. He was delighted to have found Beth and was also hoping to buy the house he was renting. Between his income and Beth's, he felt they could do that. He wanted some cash for emergencies and for anything else that may come up.

One had to know Tony in the past to really appreciate the experience of seeing him now. It felt like he was a young man with his first love and excited about life. As soon as I thought that I realized it probably was his first love and first real and honest relationship. Tony wasn't big on emoting, yet here he was like a teenager on his first date. Excited, talking fast about his plans for the future, asking me what I thought of Beth, and, after I told him how much I liked her, going on about her wonderful attributes and how much everybody seemed to like her.

Finally I said, "Tony, do you have any idea how strange it is for me to see you like this? Please don't get me wrong, and I really am impressed with and like Beth, but this isn't the Tony I'm used to. I am very happy you have found the right woman and can get this enthusiastic about life. You're giving me hope."

Tony simply smiled and nodded in agreement at my comment.

I went on to tell him about how Julie was questioning whether I was clinically depressed and how she would like to see me get assessed by a professional. I explained to Tony how that made sense and talked a little about my apathy for life in the past and lack of energy.

Tony related his experience with depression. He had found a counselor two years prior whom he had grown to rely on. She had talked him into getting meds for depression from his doctor. He thought they had helped and with the therapy from his counselor plus meetings he had managed to get sober again. He went on to tell me he had started talking about his past after being prodded by his counselor. He could talk to his counselor and felt heard and never felt judged about talking about his life.

The upshot was that he had begun to talk about his life. This was something he had not done ever. Something he had never planned on doing. He had shut the door to the past and had never wanted to open it again. He was finding out he had buried the past alive. It had come back to haunt him and if he wanted to get out of the nightmare he was caught in, he had to face it and talk about it. Talk about something he had sworn would not be on his radar again in this lifetime. He had to learn to talk about his feelings.

He looked at me and said, "Fucking feelings! Who knew?"

After a pause we both broke into laughter.

I felt like I had just witnessed something profound. Something rare and unique and something one simply did not see often in a lifetime. A psychic change. A change so profound as to rock my reality. I continued to talk with Tony but a part of me was in shock with what I had just witnessed and heard.

Tony to me was a tough guy's tough guy. I had seen him face violent and life-threatening situations without batting an eye. Emotionally he seemed so shut down that an atomic bomb could not reach his emotional life. I knew a little about his childhood and it wasn't pretty. He had offhandedly remarked once about how he had run into a foster parent he had been with for a short time. The man had abused him as a young boy. Tony had simply stated he didn't think he'd be bothering anyone else. I don't think he had but at the time I wondered if he had killed the guy.

When I thought of Tony telling me that I thought of a scene in the movie *Sleepers*. In the movie two boys who had been sodomized in a reform school ran into the guard who had abused them. Being grown men the guard didn't recognize them at first. Eventually they told him their names. When recognition came one of them dropped a pistol on the table in front of him stating they were not kids anymore. The intimation in the movie was that because of the abuse they had both become stone-cold killers. When the guard started downplaying the abuse the shooting commenced and revenge was had. The scene took place in a restaurant and they both casually walked out. It was a fabulous payback scene.

It was all the more poignant to me because I had read the book the movie was based on. And the author swears it was a true story. I saw Tony as having that type of attitude. I started thinking I would need to change how I thought Tony would act or react. I wasn't kidding though when I said it gave me hope. I figured if Tony could change then what was my excuse? That simple fact left me devoid of reason to complain or not try.

38

John had a new pastime. He had discovered baseball. He had joined a baseball league and had played in a few games. He asked if I would come and watch him play. I told him of course. I went to an early meeting one night and walked a half mile to get to a 7 p.m. game he was in. When I got to the field, I was surprised to see all the players in baseball uniforms. It was also a coed league with a pretty good disparity in ages as well.

John came over and said hello, asking me what I thought of their uniforms. I told him I thought they were pretty cool and that I felt he had been holding out on me being this was the first I had heard of all this. He assured me it had all happened so fast that it wasn't the case, and he was really happy I was here.

He told me Lilly might be coming to watch him too. I hadn't heard him mention Lilly much of late, so I was surprised to hear that. I liked Lilly but I was definitely still concerned about repercussions from the incident with the minister. When I heard of or saw Lilly, it would remind me of my exposure there.

Tony was a godsend in that I could quiet those fears by talking with him. What had happened that night I wouldn't talk about with anyone else. Tony would give me an accurate and realistic perspective on my fears. He thought I had nothing to worry about because of the minister's concern about others finding out about his abuse of Lilly. He also assured me that pedophiles like him didn't have friends that would come looking for me. They lived a solitary life with their evil. What he said made sense and I was happy he was around to remind me once in a while to keep my projections at bay.

The game started and John was playing second base. I searched my mind for John having referenced baseball in the past. I remember him talking about playing a time or two but nothing recently. I found myself excited to watch him. One of the players on the opposing team hit a ground ball to John, which he fielded easily and threw him out at first base. He looked like he had played before. He looked good out there. That fact made me very happy for some reason. I felt I could complement his skills and tease him about holding out on me. It felt like a win-win. I smiled at my own simplemindedness.

My thoughts were interrupted by Lilly walking up to me and saying hi. She had gotten new braids and was smartly dressed in pants with an attractive blouse. She looked terrific and I told her so and how nice it was to see her.

She beamed me a smile and stepped aside and started introducing someone named Corinne whom she said was her aunt. The sight of her aunt almost knocked me over. It was the singer from the club. The black jazz singer with the braids who dressed with enough colors to look like Matisse and Monet had picked them.

She was dressed like that again. As when she had been in the club it was topped off with a multicolored wrap around her braids which were tied in a bun on her head. She was dazzling. I was freaked out. She had come over to me that night in the club saying she heard I was a friend to the oppressed. My thought at the time was how the hell she could have known. I just got my answer. She was Lilly's aunt.

I took a few slow deep breaths to calm myself. I managed to say hi and we regarded each other. Nothing else came to mind to say and she didn't say anything more, but we stood looking at each other. Finally someone in the stands complained and asked us to sit down so they could see the game, which frankly I had forgotten about.

We sat down with Lilly next to me and her aunt next to her. An inning later, John came up to bat and Lilly and I yelled encouragement. He connected with a fastball that unfortunately he hit straight at the left fielder who caught it for an out. Lilly was impressed though, and we both yelled out approval.

I was watching the game but had the singer on my mind. I glanced over at her a couple of times and caught her checking me out once. That made me happy which confirmed my simplemindedness as a theme for the day.

The game passed quickly. John got a hit and fielded a few ground balls that came his way. He was a good second baseman and could get hits. A solid baseball player.

After the game we went to a local ice cream shop with Lilly and her aunt, Corinne. John hung out with Lilly while I talked to her aunt. I was smitten. There was no doubt about it. I had gone from worrying about what she knew to obsessing about how I could see her again. I wasn't sure but I thought she was interested in me as well. I had one awkward moment when I remarked how good Lilly looked. Corinne looked at me with a wry smile and said, "Thanks to you."

I wasn't ready by a long shot to open that door and said nothing. Otherwise, we hit it off famously. She was traveling some due to her singing gigs over the next month but would be back for a while after that. I asked if we could get together when she came back and she said she would like that. She said she would be singing twice a week in the pub we had met in.

She asked me to meet her there and gave me a date for her return.

"Count on it," I told her.

When they left, John and I walked back to camp. I was lost in thought when John asked me if I liked Lilly's aunt. I told him maybe and he laughed. I asked him if he liked living. He answered yes, so I told him his demise could be arranged. He laughed again so I put him in a headlock and fake punched him all over.

Then I pushed him away and said, "You should talk with the way you and Lilly were fawning over each other."

We spent the rest of the walk arguing who was the bigger bucket head. I'm not sure who won the argument.

39

Things started moving quickly. I had an intake interview for a halfway house. I was deemed a good candidate but had to wait for an open bed. Meanwhile they made an appointment with a psychologist for me. She prescribed an antidepressant and despite being a little wary of meds I started taking them. I continued going to meetings and meeting up with Julie, my sponsor. I tried to meet Tony once a week to talk with also. We had a lot in common and despite our laconic natures we were beginning to talk about stuff. We mulled over our past reasons for relapsing as we both had a strong desire to stay sober. We also both remarked on how this time it felt different. We were beginning to talk about our feelings and we both had someone we could talk with. Tony had his counselor, Grace, and I had my sponsor, Julie.

Tony went to a couple of meetings a week and had another guy he talked to regularly who he valued the way he valued our friendship. Outside of that small circle he didn't venture far for advice. We talked about not having lots of people to talk to and we realized it had soured us in the past on the program. People who were controlling or condescending were not our favorites. We solved that by limiting our personal shares with people we trusted. What others thought didn't count or didn't matter. That worked and we both felt we were solidly back in the program with a strong desire to stay sober.

That aside we were both grappling with a concept of a higher power that would work for us. Tony was leaning in the direction of a force that was abundant and shown in nature and made the trees grow and the world go round. It was something greater than himself that he could conceptualize in a way that would make sense for him. It helped him let go.

I was struggling with the harsh concept of God I had grown up with. God was judging me, watching me, controlling me, and disgusted with my performance. Julie was telling me I had projected the attributes of abusive parents and church authority figures onto God. She was encouraging me to find a God of love.

When I told her the word God conjured up control, judgement, and hellfire and damnation for me, she replied, "You need to find another name for God. Use higher power until you find something better."

I was at the point of when Julie spoke, I listened. She had given me lots of great advice, and on the rare occasion she was wrong, I still considered her advice. I talked with Tony about my higher power or God dilemma, and he was impressed with Julie's insight and advice. With that validation came a real feeling of gratitude for the blessing that was Julie in my life.

Tony and I marveled at the world of feelings. How we had trained ourselves so well to shut them down as boys. We learned to never show emotion and never give an inch. We had lived by the code and apparently the fucking code was wrong. More than wrong it had the power to kill us and kill us quickly.

We both felt we were at the point of no return when it came to drinking. Another relapse and there would be no point of trying to come back. Just stay out and drink ourselves to death. I had seen guys do it and I could identify with the despair, hopelessness, and the willingness to pay the cost of the next drink. When I thought of the despair and depression, I could see myself falling back into, death seemed like one of the better alternatives.

Tony and I had both learned that talking or acknowledging our feelings was an important component of staying sober. We now had a willingness to go to great lengths for our sobriety.

40

I got together with Sue. We had been trying for a while to get together but one of us always had something on that would interfere. Frankly with my mood and energy, I had a low sex drive. That and the fact of meeting Corinne had me questioning about continuing with Sue.

Sue looked tired and stressed. She looked a little like I felt. After a short time, I took the risk and told her so. Her work was always on the verge of getting better but continued to be difficult. A change in work responsibilities or the new director work was about to lighten the load. But they did not.

Then there was the issue of her drinking. She, too, had been in AA and had relapsed. I didn't think she drank as much as me, but it was beginning to affect her work performance. She was stressed at work then drinking to relieve the stress and stressed from the hangovers. She was in a no-win cycle. I pointed out she needed to get sober again, but she felt she was too stressed not to drink. I could remember thinking like that and tried to come up with something to say that would break through her denial. I came up blank, so I kept quiet. I felt compassion. Not just for her in her denial but also for myself and all of us who struggle with the paradoxes and conundrums of living a sober life. Breaking through denial and one's own rationalization for drinking or drugging is a bitch. Pure and simple, a bitch.

I caught her up with my news of sobriety, the treacherous world of feelings, and going to meetings. She vented about work. After a bit we were both talked out. She started kissing me and that got me in the mood. We both worked pretty diligently on relieving stress for a while. It was decent sex considering our conditions. Afterwards I felt relaxed in a way I couldn't get to without sex. I think it fair to say she did too. We lay relaxed for a while, occasionally talking and occasionally dozing for some time.

I had started out the evening wondering if this somewhat casual relationship was over. Now I felt very close to her after some passionate sex. I had read something once in a book by Marianne Williamson. She had written that at the end of a relationship one needed to love in order to let go. Or something to that affect. I wondered if that was what this was all about.

41

I met Julie at a Sunday morning meeting. Afterwards we went for lunch and took a walk and enjoyed the nice weather and the fall foliage. We sat on a rock near a lake and soaked up the sun for a bit.

She shared some of her dark times getting and staying sober. She also shared about a good friend of hers who didn't make it. She had been grieving her off and on since it had happened. Her friend had picked up after getting two years clean. She started using coke and then heroin and overdosed within a year. Her friend had suffered from severe depression. She had been suicidal off and on for a long time before and after she picked up. Julie confessed she had been afraid she would lose her friend to suicide. She wondered if the overdose was just another form of suicide for her friend.

After telling me about her friend we laid on the rock, soaking up some of the last sun we might have until spring. Suddenly I felt compelled to talk. I confessed I wasn't doing too well before I met John. I had been thinking a lot about checking out. I had been living a solitary life and had been losing my will to live.

"If John hadn't come along, I probably would be dead by now."

Julie took that in and said she had sensed a melancholy and a predilection towards depression in me, which was why she had wanted me to be assessed by a psychiatrist.

"You remind me of my friend in some ways. You both have a certain sadness and psychic weariness that I sense. That scares me because I don't want to lose another close friend."

The reference as friend surprised me. As I thought about it, I considered that yeah, being friends was how I would define it but somehow it touched me that Julie referred to me in that manner. I felt like I really never had friends. Now I had two. Tony and Julie. It was more than I had ever had. I was extremely grateful for both friends but the fact I had only two sounded lame and made me feel sad for a bit.

In the past I had briefly told Julie how John and I had met but I started telling her the whole story. She was horrified at the fact of John's beating at the hands of the two thugs and what might have happened. I told her the facts though because of the effect it seemed to have on John wanting to stay with me. How I hadn't been able to get rid of him and how eventually I didn't want him to leave.

Meeting John seemed to have been a catalyst for bringing me back to the land of the living. That and the fortuitous timing of running into Julie and getting sober. But John had started the process. Julie loved the whole story.

I told her about a lot of the things we had already been through together. I even told her about stopping the abuse that Lilly had been enduring. She asked me how I had done that.

"I told the minister it would be in his best interest to stop abusing her."

She looked at me for a long moment after that and then broke into laughter.

"If ever there was a time your penchant for violence would come in handy that would be a fortuitous moment."

It was a relief to hear her say that. Julie hated violence but she knew I didn't just talk to the minister. Still, I wasn't foolish enough to tell her how I really had convinced him.

After telling Julie about the saga of John and myself, I started telling her about the three previous years. How I had been living alone and alternating between maintenance drinking and binge drinking. Isolated and alone, slowly slipping into a quagmire of despair and despondency. Wanting to change but unable to find the will or the energy. Negativity creeping in and slowly taking hold. A single thought of suicide leading to many thoughts of suicide until *kill yourself* was the internal soundtrack of my whole day.

I confessed to Julie that I had come back to the city where I met John to prepare to do myself in. It surprised me to hear myself say that. Like I hadn't admitted that fully to myself. That had been the vague plan I had when I returned to the city and fell asleep in the weed yard after resting for a few minutes. Then I woke up to the John's screams and my life was set off on a different trajectory.

Julie was enamored of the story. She admitted she thought John and I were wonderful for each other before she heard the full story. Now she was knew we were meant to meet and be involved in each other's life.

Julie's friendship and care combined with the autumn sun to give me a feeling of warmth and happiness that was unique for me. I longed to stay here in this moment forever.

42

I was given horrendous news. I couldn't deal with it or hold onto it. I disassociated.

It felt like I was in the cockpit of a Star Wars movie. I was traveling through space. Stars were going by at a fast clip. Occasionally meteors would go by. Suddenly the scene would speed up and I was traveling faster, and the stars would almost be a blur but then it would slow down again. I was fascinated by it all. I wondered calmly how it was that I was in this position to be seeing this and traveling so.

The scene disappeared and I found myself on a beach in the middle of summer. I was thirteen and I was with my cousin Tommy, who was fourteen, and a friend of his named Bob. Tommy's father, my uncle, had taken us here. We were at Revere Beach, which was a little north of Boston on a hot sunny day in July. My uncle had gone off with some friends at one end of the beach that allowed drinking. The three of us boys were left to swim and hangout on our own.

I was fascinated and enthralled by the scene and the fact I finally made it to this beach. Coming here was talked about by city kids like it was a summertime holy grail. The beach was packed with people from the city and outlying suburbs seeking relief from the heat. The sounds of the surf breaking on the shore was intermingled with the laughter and screams of children. The sun was hot and shimmied on the water as it rose in the sky. There were families here, but it was a popular beach for local high schoolers also. There was plenty of girls that Tommy and Bob were constantly commenting on or indicating which direction the best sights were coming from. They were like radio commentators with their constant stream of comments and ratings on the girls coming and going. They were at the height of adolescent boys' fascination with girls' breasts. "Look at the tits on her," was the most common used phrase of the day.

Being two years younger, I felt less knowledgeable. My cousin and Bob were both happy to have a disciple with them that they could tutor. I rolled with it because I was so enthralled to be there. I loved it all: the water, the scenes, the heat, the sights, and, of course, the girls. The memory of Tommy with utter confidence declaring which girl had the absolute best body on the whole beach. It was one of a few happy memories I had from childhood. A fun day with my cousin and his friend. The fact that I caught a beating when I got home over I don't remember what or why couldn't ruin the good memory that day was for me.

The memory faded and I felt vague sensations tugging at my body. Or was it my psyche. It felt strange and dreamlike. Suddenly I was transported to a day of days. The hands down absolute very best day of my childhood.

A memory still vividly burned in my psyche. I, like many, had played some organized baseball since the age of nine. For a boy growing up in Southie, it made this a religious experience. A religious experience in the greatest cathedral of Boston: Fenway Park. I got to go to an opening day game at Fenway Park. The Red Sox against the Detroit Tigers.

It was a beautiful spring day with the sun shining bright in a way that only happened in April. It made the colors super vivid and the experience that more memorable. The grass was a perfectly even bright green. The infield was a rich tan color. The lines marking the out-of-bounds boundaries were a vivid white. The uniforms were bright and clean.

The sounds also seemed crisp and clean: the chatter of the ball players; the crack of the ball on the bat as the batters practiced hitting; the thump of the ball thrown by the pitcher into the catcher's mitt; the hum of the crowd as anticipation mounted with the first pitch growing close; the food and beverage hawkers shouting out their wares.

Big league baseball at Fenway.

Me and my cousins were giddy with excitement over simply being there. I was there with Tommy and his older brother, Danny. I was ten years old; Tommy was eleven, and Danny was fourteen and playing baseball in high school. Their father had hit the daily number and had bought the coveted tickets off of someone. They had an extra ticket and invited me. My father was traveling for a few days so I didn't have anyone to say, "hell no, he can't go." I slipped into a magical childhood moment by default.

I could still see, taste, smell, and mostly feel that day. We ate hot dogs, drank Coke, and marveled at the crowd and the energy in the stadium. I know Roger Clemens pitched but it was such an overload of sensory experience I don't really remember much else about the game other than the Red Sox won. It was a moment in my life that made me believe magic was possible.

The tugging and noises that were vague had become a crescendo. The violent shaking got my attention. I was being pushed and pulled by someone. As if coming out of a soundproof room I suddenly heard someone's urgent voice.

"You're scaring me! Are you alright? Are you alright? Say something please!"

It was Julie, my sponsor, and I wondered why she was shaking and screaming at me. Then I remembered. There had been an accident.

Tony and John had been in Tony's truck when someone had run a red light and smashed into it. She had told me Tony was dead and John was in the hospital. She didn't know more about John's condition.

I stood there taking deep breaths trying to take it in. I had disassociated. The news had pushed me into the netherworld. The desire to go back there was huge, but I fought it off to deal with the horror of what I had been told.

I focused in on Julie as she kept asking if I was alright.

Finally I told her, "No, I am not alright, I am definitely not alright. I am a very long fucking way from alright."

43

We went to the hospital to see John. When we got there, we found out he was in a coma. Ekaterina and Cora were already there and had talked to a doctor about John's condition. Ekaterina told me they had heard from a friend who had heard from a friend about the accident and had come straight to the hospital. I told them I really appreciated them being there to do what they could for John in his time of need.

"John has been a very good friend to both of us and we are happy to do whatever we can," Ekaterina replied.

I sat down and tried to quiet my mind. I couldn't. It was racing all over the place. I was confused and unprepared for the torrent of conflicting feelings that felt like a tsunami of emotion. Impossible to get a handle on any of it. I did what I did best. Looked emotionally blank. Hid the torrent.

Julie came over and sat down next to me. She asked if I was okay. I simply said, "No."

She sighed and leaned her head on my shoulder and held my hand. It helped. It made me feel like I was not alone in this. At least for the time being. After an hour, a doctor came out and spoke with us. John had suffered a serious head injury. He was stable but in a coma.

The complete extent of his head injuries wouldn't be known 'til he regained consciousness.

He went on for a bit, but the gist seemed to be we were in a waiting game.

John would be transferred to a room soon where we could visit him. An hour later we were by his side. Julie, Ekaterina, and Cora took turns talking to him, telling John they were there and praying and pulling for him. They all wept. I held his hand silently for a time. I searched for a prayerful state. If ever I believed in God I would certainly like that God to manifest a miracle or some healing here. I was still numb. One thing I knew: I didn't want John to die.

Eventually everyone left and I asked the nurses if I could stay in a chair in the room overnight. They allowed it. I talked a little to John and told him I was there with him. He was hooked up to monitors and it seemed like the beeping and noises of the machines slowed when I talked to him. I took that as a good sign. I settled into the chair after a while and nodded off. I slept fitfully off and on.

In the early morning, nurses came in and tended to him for a bit. I had to wait outside the room until they were finished. Later that morning the doctor who had spoken to us the day before came by to check on him. I asked him if there was anything I should watch for. He reiterated that physically John looked to be okay, and all his vital signs were good. The head injury was the big question mark, and we wouldn't have that answered until John came out of the coma.

I asked about the length of the average coma after something like a bad accident. He said it could be anywhere from a day or two up to months or years. Again, it was a waiting game and impossible to know right then. I thanked the doctor for his time and help.

A waiting game seemed to be the bottom line. My mind wandered off into an even more difficult area. Tony had died. I had thought about his fiancée, Beth. I wondered if I should try to reach out to her soon. An hour later she came by to check on John. I went to her and hugged her when I saw her.

"I don't have words," I said.

She hugged me and wept. She held me and wept way past awkward. To my credit I let her and didn't try to discourage it.

Eventually we talked. She was making arrangements for Tony's wake which would occur three days hence at a local funeral home. The only living relative that Beth knew about was a distant cousin who may or may not make the funeral. She had gotten support and solace from her friends and some good people in the program.

She felt it didn't help much. She was bereft. She had waited a long time to meet Tony, and in a flash, he was gone. Never mind the fact of how happy Tony was. I agreed with her on that.

"I had never seen Tony happy like he was with you."

It had been on the periphery of my mind that the Tony of the brutal and hard life had found a little piece of the sun after decades of violence and hardcore addiction. And what? Killed in a fucking car accident. I found it too painful to contemplate.

Beth looked at me and asked, "Why?"

I had no answer for her as she started weeping again.

Cora and Ekaterina came by, and the three of them grieved together. They had gotten to know Tony through John and they liked him. They really liked Paula and had hung out with her separate from Tony.

I watched them cry together with a little envy. I had been watching women cry my whole life. It seemed cathartic. I had watched woman weep and wail and then after a time go about their business. Like they had gotten the pain out. Or at least some of it.

I couldn't remember the last time I cried. I was becoming aware there may be a cost to not crying. I felt like the grief wasn't moving. Somehow it was stuck and remained within me. Did crying move grief out and through one? I couldn't answer that, but it was one more thing that made me feel like an emotionally deficient person.

Julie came by and talked me into leaving for a while. She wanted me to get something to eat and change my clothes. It made sense so I did it. I came back right after. I was determined to keep vigil for a while in case John came out of his coma. I wanted someone he knew to be there. Preferably me.

44

Three days later, John was in the same condition. It was still a waiting game. Julie came by to take me to Tony's wake. It wasn't something I was looking forward to. There was a good crowd at the funeral parlor. I knew many of the people from AA. There was also a nice contingent of Beth's friends, coworkers, and family. It was a sad affair. Beth wept off and on all night. In the receiving line she introduced me as one of Tony's best friends. I was moved by that and told her so. She started crying again and we hugged. She said she was praying all the time for John's recovery, knowing how much we meant to each other. I couldn't think about losing John. I was barely coming to terms with losing Tony. I hoped Beth would find peace, but I didn't think that would be quick or easy.

The following day was the funeral. Another somber affair. I was a pall bearer, which was good because I had to focus on something other than what had happened. Afterwards I said my goodbyes and went back to the hospital. Back to my vigil. I would leave during the day for a few hours and would sleep in the chair and keep watch every night. I was determined to do this for a while. I hoped and kept expecting him to come out of the coma and start asking me questions.

He used to annoy me to no end with his endless and persistent questions. I would have done anything to hear one now.

Days turned into weeks. Every day I would leave and get something to eat and maybe change my clothes. I still had a camp about one mile from the hospital. My clothes, tent, and sleeping bag were there. I started hiding my gear and tent under some brush while I was absent. At night I would return to the hospital and stay in the chair by his bed. Cora, Ekaterina, and Julie would come by at least every other day. They would bring other acquaintances of John on occasion. One was another street kid who admired John. The others were friends of theirs from the program who got friendly with John also.

Three weeks into my vigil, Lilly came by. She was with her aunt, Corrine. Corrine had been on my mind before the accident in a big way. Seeing her reminded me I had a different focus now. Getting together with her was far from my mind because of the circumstances.

Lilly walked over to the bed and grabbed one of John's hands and put it on her cheek. She stayed liked that staring at John for several minutes. She cried silent tears. Corrine expressed her sympathy on the loss of Tony. Lilly had run into Ekaterina somewhere and had heard the story. She had immediately started harassing Corrine to take her to the hospital to check on John. Eventually she put John's hand down and came over and gave me a hug. She held me silently for several minutes. Her head came up to my chest and she just stood there hugging me not letting go. A month ago, I would have considered this awkward, unbearable even. Today I was touched and appreciated the gesture from someone who loved John as much as I did. She let go and looked up at me with tears running down her face.

"I know how much you love John," I said. "We both appreciate how much you care and the fact that you're here."

She didn't say anything but hugged me again and held on for another five minutes. When they were ready to leave Corrine came over to me and gave me a hug.

I had stopped worrying about any fallout from the minister. Corrine's gratitude was sincere so I trusted she wouldn't hurt me with any of her knowledge. Since John got hurt, I felt like nothing else really mattered all that much. Including any fallout over the minister.

Lilly and Corrine were a bright spot in the darkness I felt enveloping me. Julie, Cora, and Ekaterina were steady visitors who I appreciated, but we had run out of things to say. They had run out of new ways to say, "keep the faith," "stay hopeful," or "I'm sure he'll be alright." It had been a month and I could feel myself on a downward slide. I could feel the "triple d's" taking me down: despair, despondency, and depression. Leading to a blackhole of hopelessness that I wasn't sure I had the capacity to deal with again. I had been there before but had been somewhat ignorant of where I was until I had crawled out of it. I didn't think I would last three weeks the way I felt previously for at least three years. It was too dark.

It scared me enough to talk with Julie. I mitigated my emotional condition somewhat so as not to worry her inordinately. I knew she was already concerned about me. After talking with her I agreed to hit a daytime AA meeting when I took my daily break from the hospital.

Meetings could induce a better mood.

45

I kept my vigil. I tried to hit a daytime meeting when I took my daily break. There were several noontime meetings I could walk to. I would sit and listen and on occasion share my concerns over the health of a close friend or my sadness over a dead one. Most of the participants were helpful and might say something like, "I hope your friend pulls through" and "I'm sorry to hear about the loss of your friend." I appreciated them. Then there were some who had to give me their litany of death and hard times they had stayed sober through. I wondered what they thought that would do. To me it signified nothing and meant less. To act like you could compare one death and its significance from one person to another seemed to me to be the height of chutzpah. Yet some had no problem with it. I had no problem walking up to them after the meeting and telling them not to reference my share again. They would all start to give me an explanation which I simply wouldn't listen to. I would walk away and pray to the God that I wasn't sure I believed in to remove the desire to smash someone's face on the ground several times.

Maybe it was the prayer or the fact that I didn't want to tell Julie about being violent, but I didn't hit anybody. Real growth considering with John in a coma I really didn't care about much. Hitting somebody often just felt like a good idea at times. Another month went by. Two months isn't all that long a time but when you are waiting for someone to regain consciousness, it could feel like forever. Especially if you have been with him twenty-one hours of every day.

I had taken to talking to John. I would tell him how much I missed his endless questions. I recalled most of the annoying things he had asked me or said. I told him I couldn't believe how much one could miss that shit. Then I would get more honest and tell him I couldn't believe how much I missed that shit. Then I would sit there feeling sad holding his hand or arm. I would watch his face and extremities looking for a sign of awareness or cognition. Nothing.

The vigil went on.

One day after leaving the hospital to change, eat, and hit a meeting, I saw a guy I had been friendly with named Brendan. He had been in program and had relapsed. I knew depression was also part of his struggle. I started walking toward him to say hello when he spotted me across a plaza in the downtown section of the city.

Our eyes locked as he saw me walking toward him. He shook his head no in a sudden, emphatic move. It was such a dramatic and precise action I stopped walking and stared at him. He then turned and quickly walked away. I had talked to him once after he had relapsed and knew he was hurting. I thought this action indicated he was done trying to get sober. He didn't want to hear it anymore. He was drinking himself out. I briefly considered chasing him. Somehow it felt more dignified to leave him alone with his decision if that was the case. At any rate he didn't want to talk with me. I figured he would last maybe a month. I watched him turn a corner thinking I might never see him again.

I had really wanted to talk with him about my mood. I was able to relate with him. He had been a casual friend. I was hoping to include him in my small circle of people I related to. A guy I could talk with. I had recently lost Tony. I felt like I'd also lost Brendan. Sometimes I wondered about the dark side of God. Life often felt cruel to me.

46

Another month passed. I was losing hope that John would recover. I didn't want to, and I tried not to, but it was becoming difficult. I wondered if he'd be the same even if he did come out of the coma.

Sometimes the meetings helped for a short time. Then reality would set back in. Julie, Ekaterina, and Cora would all come by a couple of times a week. It always helped to see them. There were a lot of hours in between their visits though. Life was looking dark and bleak again. It felt that way too. I was beginning to feel the way I did just before John had come into my life. Alone and not really wanting to change that. Comfortable wherever that might take me. It felt like I was beginning a slow steady slide to oblivion. I was okay with that. Which is what scared me.

Being okay with it meant that was where I was heading.

Oblivion.

I was at a meeting when I heard someone talk about someone dying. It turned out it was Brendan. Found dead in the streets somewhere from alcohol poisoning. Old school: straight up drank himself to death. Almost a month to the day after I had seen him last. It made me sad to hear about. I could relate to and was friendly with Brendan.

I seriously wondered if his fate would become mine. A week later I found out.

I was in front of an inviting bar. I could taste the whiskey and the beer chaser. Not something I hadn't dealt with before but this time I simply didn't care. I'd been fighting the drink hard for several weeks. This day I had no defense against it. I went in and ordered a shot of Jack Daniels and a draft beer. The whiskey went down and gave me that expectant warm feeling. I thought it was the least it could do seeing how it was probably going to drag me through hell. That thought turned out to be prophetic.

I blacked out after the third shot. I woke up in a jail cell, hungover, and feeling beat up. Turned out I had been beat up. I had no memory, and I was afraid to ask anyone. But a guy in the cell next to me said I had dried blood on my face and multiple cuts.

My hangover turned into a migraine. The off and on nausea and pounding in my head demanded all my attention for a bit. When that pain lessened, I found out I was being charged with assaulting an officer, disturbing the peace, and drunk and disorderly conduct. Also, it was Saturday. No arraignment or chance to make bail until Monday.

Exactly as promised. Misery returned. Well, if it was coming back you might as well make it quick. Monday came torturously slowly. I hadn't been in a jail cell in a while and the amenities were about the same. Nonexistent. That and the whole weekend being one horrible hangover. Never mind the guilt and remorse about letting everyone down yet again. It led to a strong desire not to return here when I got out.

Monday morning, I was off to court. The judge set my bail at $5,000. I was resigned to going to prison as I didn't have that kind of money. Nor did I have the $500 that I needed to make bail through a bondsman. That fact set me off on a self-condemnation spree that left me aching for another drink to just frigging stop the pain of feeling.

Before I was put back in the van returning to prison, I was told

I had made bail. Or someone had made bail for me. I was released. When I left the courthouse, I expected Julie to be there. She wasn't. It was Sue.

I asked her, "Did you bail me out?"

"Yes." She went on to tell me she had actually been at a meeting when she overheard someone talking about me. She had started going to meetings again about three weeks earlier. She inquired and was told the word was out that I had gotten picked up for assaulting an officer during a relapse. She called the police to confirm and found out I would be arraigned today.

I thanked her and told her I was still hurting from the arrest and hangover. I asked if I could go to her place to clean up and maybe sleep for a bit. To my relief she agreed and gave me the key to her place. I debated telling her she really ought not give her key out to someone in relapse. I decided against it because I really needed a safe place to sleep.

Sue was good to me. She was grateful for my friendship. During the times we got together for sex I had apparently soft sold her on returning to meetings. She needed time to go back but really appreciated my reminders and soft approach.

She had gotten sober for four months several years previous. She went out but was now ready to come back. She was hitting a meeting a day and was ready to jump back in so to speak. She was appreciative that I was around giving her those reminders and being a power of example. I had told her some highlights or lowlights to be more accurate of my life and she considered it remarkable I had made it to AA.

At least before my relapse. When she had heard I had relapsed she wanted to help and there we were. She graciously and generously offered me the use of her apartment for a while. I really appreciated that because I wanted to get back to the hospital and my vigil. I hadn't checked on John in four days and felt anxious to get back there.

It was Wednesday evening before I had recovered and healed up enough to be presentable in public. I still had the shadow of a shiner and a few cuts healing but felt ready to venture out. When I got to the hospital, I found John in the same condition as before. There had been no improvement.

The nurses asked me where I had been. I sheepishly told them I had a little trouble and told them I'd prefer not to talk about it. The nurses had been great and were often kind and supportive of me as I kept my vigil. After constantly seeing me several had inquired about my relationship with John. Many of them thought I was his father. I told them we had become friends after I had helped John with some bullies. They loved that story. They also thought my devoted vigil was a wonderful thing.

They were rooting for improvement in John's condition also. I found that touching and helpful for me to keep the faith. Faith or no faith, however, John's condition was not improving. I didn't think I'd be able to come to terms with that. Losing John would be the loss which put me over the top. It would put me solidly in a category where one had serious trouble coming to terms with their existence.

I started my routine again of keeping vigil with John. l would leave for a few hours to eat, change, and go to a meeting. I had relapsed and mentioned that in a short share but felt reluctant to talk more. AA was powerful. I might not want to live anymore but I still didn't want to drink. One slip and I had a serious assault charge to deal with.

I had been dreading running into Julie. One day I was at an early evening meeting when Julie walked in a few minutes late. I had felt embarrassed and ashamed to talk to her because of my relapse. After the meeting I waited outside for her as she talked with several people. I figured I'd be smart and face the music now.

She came out after a bit and just looked at me for a moment. We talked for a bit, and I told her about my relapse and current mental state. After some gentle encouragement to get reinvolved in a big way, she embraced me in a warm hug. Eventually she backed off and looked me in the eye again and simply said, "You need to find your higher power now." She said that with tears in her eyes and then just walked away.

This encounter with her left me in shock. No recriminations, no lecture, no guilting or shaming. Who the hell was this woman? I felt she had an eerie ability to see me and seemingly read my mind. My mind was reeling. *What did this all mean? What did she mean that I need to find my higher power now?* The encounter with Julie was so different from what I had expected. Plus, I felt like she knew. She knew I was having a serious issue with despair. I didn't want to drink anymore but I didn't want to be here either. I had made a decision. I was going to check out. Not this moment but it was coming.

47

I kept my routine up. Most of the day with John and leave for a few hours to eat and hit a meeting and change my clothes. I kept going to meetings because it kept me from reaching for a drink. I didn't want to drink, blackout, and end up in Timbuktu after having killed someone or gotten twenty tattoos or something. Both of those things seemed like real possibilities after my last binge. They said I assaulted a police officer. I may have. I may not have. It didn't matter because I couldn't remember a thing. Might as well be guilty as charged. One good thing about killing myself would be I wouldn't have to face that charge. I'd be gone.

I felt like I needed four or five days to prepare myself. During that time I needed to stay sober. I grimaced as I thought, *I have to get my affairs in order*. Sardonically I added, *I need to split up my assets of some clothes, some camping gear, and about $200*. All my worldly possessions. I thought about that for a moment. No family, no kids, and just $200. It felt sad in a way that was beyond poignant. One of those moments where I thought if I knew how to cry I would. With Tony dead and John in the hospital I seemed to be having more than my fair share of them.

I wanted to prepare myself emotionally. It wasn't every day one killed oneself. I wasn't going to make a failed attempt at it. One attempt, one death.

I had been staying at Sue's place for about a week. I needed to leave there because I didn't want her feeling responsible somehow. She had started really chasing sobriety. She had been going to two meetings a day for two weeks. It wasn't a long time, but it seemed to represent a change in attitude.

I hoped I really had helped her as she had described. It would be one of a few positive good deeds in a drunken, violent life. I left her a note saying how much I valued her friendship and help in my time of need. I wrote a second letter that I would mail just before my final act. In that note I expounded on the wonderful qualities she had and how much she had to offer the world. Also, how nice it was to have her as a friend. I explained my final act was in no way any reflection on her.

I went out to my campsite and found my gear where I had hidden it. I set up my tent and checked that my sleeping bag was still nice and dry. It was December and it was cold out. I wanted to make sure all my gear was intact and usable. I was planning to stay in the woods the next two nights. I liked camping in the cold weather, but I needed workable gear. I checked my stash of pills. I had been in a hard place about a year and half ago and because of that I had acquired a lethal amount of opioids. I would prefer a gun to pills just so I could feel more pain or more of something. I didn't have the funds for a gun, and I didn't have the energy to hunt one down. The gun I had with the minister I had tossed. So opioids it was. An all-American death. An overdose of opioids.

After I set everything up, I went and got something to eat and got ready for my vigil with John. I spent my night with John awake in a chair in the room. I thought about the profound effect that this young man had had in my life. I had gone from trying to get rid of him to keeping vigil and praying for his recovery that apparently wasn't

coming. I thought about how we met. He had actually stopped me
from possibly killing one of his perpetrators. The evil one. I remember how stunned I was at his request after the beating and ordeal he
had been through, and how relieved I was the next day that I hadn't
killed him.

Then he had asked me not to call him kid. All the shit John had
been through, and he still had courage. Every time I thought of my
relationship with John and how I felt about him, I would think of him
asking me not to call him kid. He had endured a vicious beating and
had almost been raped. I had saved him from that, and he asks me not
to call him kid. Like it was more important that I respect him than
that I saved him from the worst experience of his life. To me that was
representative of John. Courage and tenacity and maybe even fool-
ishness in the face of adversity and dealing with hard situations. Also,
the emotional availability and knowing what he wanted. When I was
his age, if someone called me kid I would either live with it or hit him
depending on his age and who it was.

Then John loved to talk. He was always chattering on about
something. In the beginning I had found that very annoying but in
time had come to look forward to it. It was hard to believe how much
I missed his chatter. He would also talk about his feelings all the time.
I had almost told him to shut the fuck up about his feelings when I
was hungover once. But somehow, I knew what he was saying was
important to him. I was at times uncomfortable knowing I didn't have
his emotional maturity. The ability to recognize and talk about feelings. I had shut mine down a long time ago. With sobriety they had
started to come up. I had started viewing John as a power of example
in this regard. Now that I thought of it, he was a power of example
in a lot of regards.

It hit me hard. The idea that I wasn't helping John anymore; John
was helping me. The whole idea of John being the helper was shock-
ing to me. I thought about it some more. Truly John had been keeping

me going not the other way around. He had even been sharing some of his earnings with me. Damn, I thought, I wouldn't get the chance to thank him in person.

Other memories came to mind. Going fishing. He taught me how to fish. We had become closer sitting on a rock fishing. And it was fun. Fun was something I knew little about. John had taught me about having fun.

And the friends he made. His friend Lilly. He got me to intervene in her abuse when I was sober no less. That's what I'd call going above and beyond as a friend.

And Cora and Ekaterina. They were no nonsense, tough as nails young women who were determined not to ever be used by anyone. Yet these two hardcore street kids loved and respected John. Because John was a hell of a good friend and a hell of a good guy, and they knew that. And what did I know? Mostly I didn't know what I knew or didn't know anymore. But I knew one thing. I loved John. I tried to think if I had ever told him that. I came up blank. I wish I had but I wasn't too upset with myself. I knew John knew I was emotionally shut down. Still, it would have been nice to have told him that.

Hell, I thought, *I can tell him now*. I dragged my chair over next to the bed. I grabbed his hand and took a breath. *Damn*, I thought, *he's in a coma and this is still difficult.* Eventually I started. I told him how much I appreciated our friendship and all the things that I didn't even know he was helping me with. And how damn proud I was of him and his courage and his character and who he was. Eventually I got around to it: I told him I loved him. And I sat there in the chair with a stirring in my soul and something shifted a wee bit inside of me. A few more of these sad, poignant moments and I might actually have tears in my eyes.

A few moments later I said, "Okay, okay what are we, a couple of girls at a sweet sixteen party?"

Then in my mind I could hear him laughing at that because it was the type of thing I would say to him to make him laugh. Then I could hear him saying, "You are such a bucket head." Then I would push him, and he would push me back. So I would put him in a headlock and fake punch him and so on.

My reverie of our times together was broken when the shift changed and the 8:00 a.m. nurses came in. It was time. The nurses changed and bathed him in the morning. One of them asked me if there had been any change in his demeanor during the night.

"No but we had a great conversation."

She looked at me strangely. I walked over and grabbed John's hand one last time and silently said goodbye. Then I left. I felt at peace. I had a few other things to do before I checked out but the important one was done. I had told John that I loved him.

48

I headed out to a local diner I favored for breakfast. I felt strangely at peace. I had felt calmer since I had decided to check out. After having said goodbye to John I felt even more at ease.

Originally, I thought that the act of making a firm decision even if it was difficult was why I was peaceful. It was more than that. It was the acknowledgement of a deep exhaustion and weariness of the daily act of living. I felt like I'd been fighting my whole life. Physically, emotionally, intellectually; in all ways and forms. Fighting for respect, fighting for revenge, fighting for a drink, fighting not to drink. Fighting to save my mother, fighting to get away from my mother. Fighting to get away from my father. Fighting for the family and ultimately fighting to get as far away from my family as possible. Fighting for the sheer will of one more time getting in the ring and taking a swing no matter how badly beat up I was. Willing myself to do something, face one more day, do whatever.

Not having to will myself or to fight or to get beat up or hungover or anything seemed like a relief.

What I was going to do was a bit drastic, but I still felt a relief. With those thoughts I ordered my breakfast. I had intended to wait 'til tomorrow but felt like today would be fine as there was nothing really left to do. I splurged and ordered bacon and sausage with my eggs as I didn't have to worry about my arteries. I smiled at my joke. Frankly, I never worried about my arteries. That was an emotionally and financially sound person's worry. I was sure I'd never given my arteries a second thought.

While I waited for my breakfast, I looked over the letter I'd written Julie. It needed a little editing, but I liked what I had written. I told her she was the most remarkable person I'd ever met. When I first met her, she was a mess, completely hooked on drugs and alcohol. When I ran into her eight years later, she was a lawyer and clean and sober in program for eight years. But more than becoming a lawyer, she had become a remarkable person. She was kind and considerate and helpful to people without being a pushover. She sponsored people like me and did pro bono work for women in need. And you could talk to her about all kinds of different things. Her knowledge and wisdom were unmatched in my experience.

I wanted to let her know she was a ray of sunlight in a life of seemingly perpetual darkness. The fact that I decided not to continue life was no reflection on her. I worked on the letter until I was satisfied with what I had written. I included a letter to Cora and one to Ekaterina in the envelope I would mail to Julie. I asked Julie to get the letters to them. I thanked them for being friends with John and told them how much I enjoyed their company and friendship. I asked them both to check on Julie once in a while if they could. With that I sealed up the envelope and finished both the bacon and sausage.

I left the diner and headed for a mailbox I knew of not too far from the path I needed to get to camp. I mailed the envelope to Julie and the one to Sue. It struck me that I was mailing nothing to family members. As I thought about it, I felt okay about that. I was Irish and tight with relatives I was not. Any personal information I had given to relatives usually got me ridiculed in one form or another. I had stopped that a long time previous. Which made it hard to be close with anyone.

I made my way to camp. The weather was about as nice as it got this time of year. The sun was out and there was no wind, which made the cold air feel good. On my way to camp something was nagging at my consciousness. Just as I got to my campsite, I realized what it was.

It involved a conversation I had with Julie. It was third step stuff. We had been discussing trusting God and having a relationship with God. I had described a firm belief that God and involvement in AA would keep me away from a drink. I had faith in God for that. Otherwise, I didn't trust or had a problem trusting God with anything else. God was a fierce, judgmental, and punishing entity.

Julie had explained that was okay and that I may need to go through my own process to find a God of my understanding. The step wording was a "a power greater than myself." She encouraged me to find a higher power that I could trust.

We had kicked this around many times in conversations that we had. She had been very patient and actually liked talking about it because it was a process she had been through also. Her higher power was a feminine deity. Julie seemed to like to talk about the process that she went through to find her higher power. One day in the middle of a conversation she had grabbed my arm and said, "When I ask sincerely, my higher power will move mountains to get me what I need. My life is an example of that."

I didn't get a chance to ask her to expound on that. Other people had joined us, and the conversation had moved on.

I formulated an idea. I thought it didn't really matter because I would be dead in a few hours. I didn't have enough time for my higher power to work in my life. I decided I'd give my higher power one hour to give me a sign. A sign that I would know was a message to continue to live. When in the next three minutes I wasn't struck by lightning, I felt disappointed.

I went about getting ready. For me it just meant getting my pills and sitting quietly on the ground. I wondered if I'd get any props for dying sober. I thought of going out drunk but decided I really would rather be sober. Good or bad it was a serious decision I had made to do a serious act. And I discovered I really, really didn't want to be drunk anymore. Even if I only had an hour left. I was done with alcohol.

I thought about my life. It made me feel sad. I felt like I had endured a mountain of pain and chaos just to get to that point. And there was a sad ending. Despite the sadness there was a relief in my decision also. I was bone weary tired. The past three to four years, it was with great effort and will I faced each day. Julie called it depression and felt it would get better. I couldn't see it. Before the accident I was willing to try for that solution. With Tony dead and John basically gone I couldn't muster the will anymore. I was done. My decision felt right. I took a deep breath and sighed. I felt sadder still.

I started to take deep breaths and tried not to think too much. I was almost ready.

49

My solitude was suddenly disturbed. I could hear people walking nearby. I felt a deep anger. Now some asshole has to find the trail that led to this camp? This camp was hard to find and rarely if ever did I get disturbed when I was here. I thought, *Maybe I'll kill the intruders before myself.*

I stood up to face whoever it was I heard moving toward me. It was Cora and Ekaterina. They came into the small clearing where the camp was and immediately bent over and put their hands on their knees trying to catch their breath. They had been running and looked exhausted. Cora started talking and was interrupted by her breathlessness.

Startled I finally blurted out, "What the hell are you two doing here?"

A moment later Cora started with Ekaterina ending the sentences, saying that they had been looking all over for me for the last two hours. This was the third camp that they had checked out. I wondered how they knew I had two other camp spots I used when I was in this city. The question of why they were looking for me got interrupted when I heard one of them say John had sent them.

"What do you mean John sent you?"

"We went to the hospital two hours ago," Ekaterina said. "When we got there, John was awake and had implored us to go and find you. We were elated that he had come out of the coma, but he kept asking us to go find you and that it was urgent that we find you soon. He had given us directions to all three of the camps that he thought you might be at."

"This is very hard to believe," I said. "I was at the hospital three hours ago and John was still in a coma." I stared at them trying to discern what was real or not.

"John told us that you might be thickheaded hearing this news," Cora said. "He told us to tell you don't be a bucket head and listen to them."

I looked from one to the other trying to take it all in. I was in shock. *John is okay? Out of the coma?* It was hard to wrap my mind around the possibility. I had been hoping for this outcome for so long, it seemed impossible. I kept staring at Cora and then Ekaterina waiting for a sign this wasn't true. None came. Cora had given me solid proof with the bucket head comment. And why would they lie? And how would they know of this camp if John hadn't told them? It slowly began to sink in that John was out of the coma. I stood there with my mouth agape for several moments. Finally, Cora said, "Come with us. Let's go to the hospital to see John."

That was when I remembered what I had been about to do. I was still in a semi-trance that my preparations had put me in. Then I remembered I had asked for a sign. With a one-hour deadline. We were thirty minutes into that hour. I had asked God for a sign for me to keep living.

The girls had seen John several hours ago and started on their quest to find and inform me of John being out of the coma. An hour ago, I had asked for a sign. So I was being answered by people from an event that had started before I had asked for a sign.

I tried to take that in but ended up feeling overwhelmed. I sat down. The timing of these events and the fact that John was out of the coma and my prayer had been answered shook me to my core.

I tried to think of a more dramatic sign than what had just occurred. I couldn't think of one.

The feeling of "if I knew how to cry, I would" came to me. But it didn't stop, and I started to cry. And I kept crying. Then I lost control. Then I started to sob.

Cora and Ekaterina, shocked at this turn of events, came over and tried to console me. They watched me cry for a bit before they started crying. And I sat in the December sun with these two teenage girls awkwardly hugging me and wept for a long time.

ACKNOWLEDGEMENTS

I have wanted to write for a long time. I always thought that I would start and eventually come out with a finished project having done it alone. It didn't work like that. It took a village and then some.

I would like to start by thanking the numerous people and friends who offered encouragement and would agree to read pieces of my writing. Some of those are Nicole Brazio, Bill McQuade, Paula Caramadre, Maria Caramadre, Kevin Costello, Stephen Donovan, Mary Dixon, Mary Chapman, Sheila Broderick, Kerry Courtney, Betty Singletary, Jim Chapin, Guy Thompson, and John Kafalas.

Thanks to family who have also read and encouraged me: Tom Casserly, Mary Beasley, Barbara Nelli, Cathy Casserly, Ellen and Marguerite Farrell.

Apologies to those I overlooked or didn't remember.

A special thanks to Jim Stahl who read my book and gave me detailed positive feed back.

A thank you to Nastia Ross for her inspiration.

Stephen Donovan, Bill McQuade, Jim Stahl, John Roarke and Maggie Kozel were kind enough to read and then give me a quote about the book. A special thanks to all of them for their creative descriptions.

I would like to thank Trisha Giramma for her work in editing the book.

Thanks to Stillwater Publishing: Steve and Dawn Porter for their help in editing and publishing.

A special thanks to Grace Dulude. A dual gift to me as a gifted therapist and a Yogi.

I have been in a writing group for many years. I continually sign up for the next one as it has been instrumental in my process. All former members of the group have been helpful. Thanks to all for the kind, encouraging and uplifting words I've been given. The latest iteration became a record-long group because of covid. A special thanks to the members of that group, who are Karen Lee, Larry Rand, Maggie Kozel, Trisha Giramma and Elizabeth Quincy.

The leader and creator of this particular writing group is Lauren Sarat. She has worked at major publishing houses in New York as an editor and book developer. She has also taught creative fiction at various colleges and universities. The simplicity of the writing group she created has belied the effectiveness it has had. It took my confidence in my writing from "this sucks" to "damn, this is good". She has been the midwife of my book. Thank you, Lauren.

This book is a work of fiction and all characters are fictional. I could not resist the impulse to use my wife Maya Breuer as a template for the jazz singer. The description of her looks, attire and affect on others when she sings is straight out of memory. All else is fictional.

Stephen King in his book "On Writing" says writing is a lonely job. Having someone who believes in you makes a difference. In my case it made a huge difference. Maya's overwhelming superlative comments on my writing seemed at times ridiculous but were always appreciated. On a shuttle bus ride in Nantucket, I was talking about my writing with a fellow passenger. Maya who was sitting in a different row other than me started comparing me to Hemingway and Dostoevsky. Finally someone asked, "Who are you to him?" When she answered, "I'm his wife," all the passengers fell out. Her support has meant the world. Thank you, Maya, and love always.

ABOUT THE AUTHOR

Stephen Casserly is a life-long resident of Rhode Island. He is a graduate of Bryant College. He retired in 2022 from being a project manager and plant acquisition specialist at a landscape firm to write full time. He has been in recovery since 1981. He is working on a second novel set in Ireland in 1860. He lives in Warwick RI, with his wife Maya Breuer.

Made in United States
North Haven, CT
18 November 2022

26903265R00117